MATH TRAILBLAZERS™

Grade 4

Unit Resource Guide
Unit 14

Chancy Predictions:
An Introduction to Probability

SECOND EDITION

A Mathematical Journey Using Science and Language Arts

KENDALL/HUNT PUBLISHING COMPANY
4050 Westmark Drive   Dubuque, Iowa 52002

A TIMS® Curriculum
University of Illinois at Chicago

UIC The University of Illinois
at Chicago

The original edition was based on work supported by the National Science Foundation under grant No. MDR 9050226 and the University of Illinois at Chicago. Any opinions, findings, and conclusions or recommendations expressed in this publication are those of the author(s) and do not necessarily reflect the views of the granting agencies.

Printed in the United States of America

1 2 3 4 5 6 7 8 9 10   07   06   05   04   03

LETTER HOME

Chancy Predictions: An Introduction to Probability

Date: _____

Dear Family Member:

Our next unit is *Chancy Predictions: An Introduction to Probability.* Your child will begin the study of probability by considering whether events are impossible, unlikely, likely, or certain. For example, it is certain that the sun will rise tomorrow; that the next animated movie will be a hit is likely; and it is, unfortunately, somewhere between unlikely and impossible that the Chicago Cubs will win the next World Series.

Students will carry out investigations that will help them develop a quantitative understanding of simple probability. Most of these investigations involve either rolling one fair number cube or using a spinner. Students will collect, graph, and analyze the data generated in these activities and then make predictions about the outcomes of random processes. They will see that although the outcomes of individual events are impossible to predict accurately, predictions are more reliable when large numbers of events are considered. For example, we cannot predict accurately which face will show in one flip of a coin, but we can safely predict that in 1000 flips, about half will be heads and about half will be tails.

What is the probability of Elvis Presley being elected President?

Probability is common in everyday life. Many games involve probability; weather predictions use probability; many judgments we make are based on estimated probabilities. The next few days will be a good time to talk with your child about probabilities you encounter every day.

Use the *Triangle Flash Cards* to continue to review the division facts for the fives, tens, twos, and square numbers.

Thank you for helping your child with math.

Sincerely,

_____

UNIT OUTLINE

Estimated Class Sessions
8–9

Chancy Predictions:
An Introduction to Probability

Pacing Suggestions

- Lesson 6 *Make Your Own Spinners* is an optional lesson. It extends students' work with probability by asking students to apply concepts to new situations.
- Lesson 7 *Prob$_e$ Quest* is an *Adventure Book* story that makes connections to language arts. Students can read the story during language arts time.

Components Key: SG = Student Guide, DAB = Discovery Assignment Book, AB = Adventure Book, URG = Unit Resource Guide, and DPP = Daily Practice and Problems

	Sessions	Description	Supplies
LESSON 1 **Chance Discussions** SG pages 384–386 URG pages 22–28 DPP A–B	1	**ACTIVITY:** Students discuss probability in qualitative and quantitative terms while constructing a probability line.	• self-adhesive notes
LESSON 2 **Bean Counter's Game** SG page 387 URG pages 29–33 DPP C–D	1	**GAME:** Students play a game that focuses on the rolls of a number cube. This game helps students develop concepts needed for Lesson 3.	• beans, small tokens, or centimeter connecting cubes • number cubes • scratch paper
LESSON 3 **Rolling a Number Cube** SG pages 388–391 URG pages 34–46 DPP E–H	2	**LAB:** Students investigate the outcome of a random process by rolling a number cube and analyzing the results. A discussion of the results is tied to both the *Bean Counter's Game* from Lesson 2 and to probability. **ASSESSMENT PAGE:** *Check-up,* Unit Resource Guide, page 44.	• number cubes • calculators

	Sessions	Description	Supplies
LESSON 4 **From Number Cubes to Spinners** SG page 392 DAB page 231 URG pages 47–54 DPP I–J	1	**ACTIVITY:** Students construct spinners that reflect the number cube investigation.	• clear plastic spinners or paper clips • protractors
LESSON 5 **Exploring Spinners** SG pages 393–396 DAB page 233 URG pages 55–67 DPP K–N	2	**ACTIVITY:** Students use models of two different spinners to explore probability. **ASSESSMENT PAGE:** *Spinners Quiz,* Unit Resource Guide, page 65.	• clear plastic spinners or paper clips
LESSON 6 **Make Your Own Spinners** SG pages 397–399 DAB pages 235–236 URG pages 68–73	– OPTIONAL LESSON – 1	**OPTIONAL ACTIVITY:** Students create spinners which reflect specific probabilities.	• clear plastic spinners or paper clips • rulers
LESSON 7 **Prob$_e$ Quest** AB pages 71–90 URG pages 74–78 DPP O–P	1	**ADVENTURE BOOK:** Students read a story and solve problems about probability.	

CONNECTIONS

A current list of connections is available at www.mathtrailblazers.com.

Software
- *Math Arena* provides practice with many math concepts.
- *Mighty Math Number Heroes* provides practice with fractions, number operations, polygons, and probability.

BACKGROUND

Chancy Predictions:
An Introduction to Probability

The lab and activities in this unit give students the opportunity to investigate the probabilities involved with number cubes and spinners. Students who have had *Math Trailblazers*™ in earlier grades will have some background in probability. Many activities in the primary grades introduce students to sampling and random variation along with basic data collection and analysis. However, this unit provides the first formal treatment of probability.

Qualitative estimates of probability (e.g., impossible, unlikely, likely, certain) often guide us in our everyday lives: *How likely is it to rain? What is the probability that this lottery ticket is a winner? What is the chance of stealing second base?* Children's qualitative understanding of probability is the starting point for this unit. Students will make statements such as "It may rain today" to begin exploring probabilities.

Probability is a measure of how likely an event is to happen. In many situations, the best we can provide is a rough, qualitative estimate of a probability.

Sometimes, however, we can quantify a probability, such as the probability of heads coming up when a coin is flipped. Probabilities can be expressed as decimals, percents, fractions, and even ratios; but, ultimately, any probability can be translated to a number between zero and one. For example, the probability of a coin landing on heads when flipped is $\frac{1}{2}$, 0.5, or 50%.

Zero probabilities are for impossible events (e.g., rolling a 7 with a standard number cube). Events that are certain, such as rolling a number less than 7 with a number cube, have a probability of one. Most events, such as rolling a 5, have probabilities between zero and one—that is, they might happen or they might not. The larger the probability of an event, the more likely that event is to happen.

One of the goals of this unit is for students to develop a quantitative understanding of probability. We focus in this unit on two relatively simple situations: rolling a single number cube and spinning various spinners.

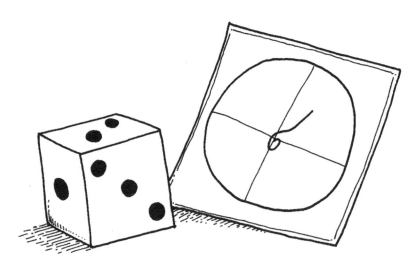

Figure 1: *A number cube and a spinner*

Sample Data

Suppose you toss one coin. You can think of your coin toss as a random experiment. That is, the coin toss is an experiment in which the outcome depends partly on luck. A coin is said to be "fair" if each side has an equal chance of coming up. If you repeat your experiment (with a fair coin) many times—that is, if you toss your coin repeatedly and if you record the outcome (heads or tails) every time—then eventually you can organize your data in a table and make a graph as shown in Figures 2 and 3.

R Result	T Number of Tosses
Heads	485
Tails	515
TOTAL	1000

Figure 2: *A sample table of 1000 tosses of a fair coin*

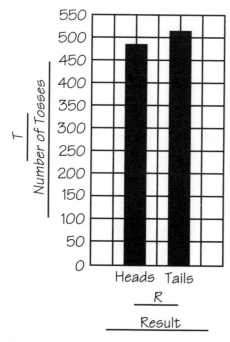

Figure 3: *A sample graph of 1000 tosses of a fair coin*

A number cube is said to be "fair" if each face has an equal chance of showing. Number cubes that are intentionally unfair are called *loaded;* number cubes that are poorly made may also be unfair. If your experiment is rolling one (fair) number cube 1000 times, then you will probably get results similar to those in Figures 4 and 5.

F Face	T Number of Times Face Appeared
1	183
2	166
3	167
4	186
5	162
6	136
TOTAL	1000

Figure 4: *A sample table of 1000 rolls of a fair number cube*

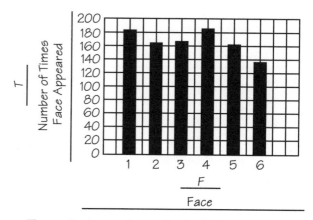

Figure 5: *A sample graph of 1000 rolls of a fair number cube*

When tossing a fair coin or rolling a fair number cube, all the outcomes are equally likely. All the bars on the graph are about the same height. On the other hand, if you spin a spinner like the one in Figure 6 one thousand times, you will probably get results similar to those in Figures 7 and 8. The outcomes are not equally likely. For example, spinning a B is more likely than an A or a C. In this unit, students will explore both kinds of experiments.

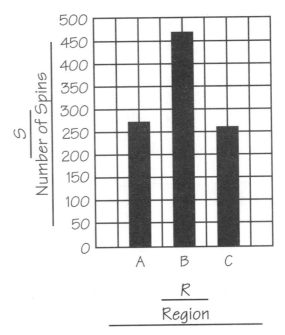

Figure 8: *A sample graph of 1000 spins of the spinner in Figure 6*

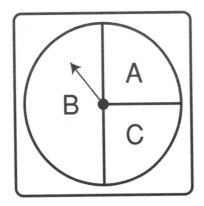

Figure 6: *A spinner*

R Region	S Number of Spins
A	270
B	472
C	258
Total	1000

Figure 7: *A sample table of 1000 spins of the spinner in Figure 6*

The Law of Large Numbers

Even when all outcomes are equally likely, they usually do not occur exactly the same number of times. Probability lets us predict *about* how often an outcome will occur, but it will not tell us *exactly* how often. The probability of flipping a head when you toss a fair coin is $\frac{1}{2}$. This means that heads can be expected to come up about $\frac{1}{2}$ of the time. The accuracy of this prediction depends on the number of times you repeat the experiment. For example, if you toss the coin only 4 times, the prediction is not a very good one. The coin might not even come up heads at all. When you toss a coin 100 times, the prediction is better. You probably will not get exactly 50 heads, but the fraction of all the tosses that is heads will be close to $\frac{1}{2}$. Another way to say this is that as we increase the number of tosses, the number of heads tends towards 50%. As you repeat an experiment more times, the probabilities involved allow you to make predictions that are more reliable. In fact, there is a proven result about what will happen when you repeat a random experiment often enough. This result is sometimes called the Law of Large Numbers.

The Law of Large Numbers says that even though individual random events or small collections of random events are unpredictable, reliable predictions can be made when large numbers of random events are involved. With enough repetitions, the fraction of times an outcome occurs (for example, "heads") approaches the probability of that outcome ($\frac{1}{2}$). For another example, even though a prediction that a 5 will come up about $\frac{1}{6}$ of the time in 12 rolls of a fair cube may not be correct, a prediction that a 5 will come up about $\frac{1}{6}$ of the time in 12,000 rolls is almost certain to be correct.

Although this unit does not discuss the Law of Large Numbers formally, students will see its effects in the lab *Rolling a Number Cube.* They will compare the results they obtain from rolling a number cube 60 times with the class's data of several hundred rolls. They will see that the heights of the bars are more even (reflecting the equal probabilities of the faces) on the class's graph of the larger number of rolls.

One of the most commonly held incorrect beliefs about probability relates to the Law of Large Numbers. Suppose a number cube is being rolled repeatedly and a 4 fails to appear in 20 consecutive rolls. Is the probability of a 4 appearing on the next roll more than, less than, or equal to one-sixth? Many people will say that since a 4 can be expected to come up one-sixth of the time in a large number of rolls, it must somehow be more likely to come up this next time because "we're due for a 4." Such a conclusion is false. The number cube has no memory that it has exhibited a deficient number of 4s. The probability of 4 coming up remains the same— $\frac{1}{6}$. What the Law of Large Numbers says about rolling a number cube is that eventually the results will even out (if the cube is fair). It does not say anything about any one roll.

Predictions

Predicting the outcome of a random process is a practical skill. People who know what to expect from buying a lottery ticket, for example, can make a more rational decision than people who have only their hopes to guide them. People who know what to expect from a 1 in 10,000 risk can judge reasonably what should be done instead of acting solely out of fear.

Assessment Indicators

- Can students collect, organize, graph, and analyze data?
- Can students make and interpret bar graphs?
- Can students use fractions to give the probabilities of events?
- Can students use probabilities to make predictions?
- Do students demonstrate fluency with the division facts for the 2s, 5s, 10s, and square numbers?

OBSERVATIONAL ASSESSMENT RECORD

(A1) Can students collect, organize, graph, and analyze data?

(A2) Can students make and interpret bar graphs?

(A3) Can students use fractions to give the probabilities of events?

(A4) Can students use probabilities to make predictions?

(A5) Do students demonstrate fluency with the division facts for the 2s, 5s, 10s, and square numbers?

(A6) _____

(A7) _____

Name	A1	A2	A3	A4	A5	A6	A7	Comments
1.								
2.								
3.								
4.								
5.								
6.								
7.								
8.								
9.								
10.								
11.								
12.								
13.								

Name	A1	A2	A3	A4	A5	A6	A7	Comments
14.								
15.								
16.								
17.								
18.								
19.								
20.								
21.								
22.								
23.								
24.								
25.								
26.								
27.								
28.								
29.								
30.								
31.								
32.								

Daily Practice and Problems

Chancy Predictions:
An Introduction to Probability

Two Daily Practice and Problems (DPP) items are included for each class session listed in the Unit Outline. The first item is always a Bit and the second is either a Task or a Challenge. Refer to the Daily Practice and Problems and Home Practice Guide in the *Teacher Implementation Guide* for further information on the DPP. A Scope and Sequence Chart for the DPP can be found in the Scope and Sequence Chart & the NCTM *Principles and Standards* section of the *Teacher Implementation Guide.*

A DPP Menu for Unit 14

Eight icons designate the subject matter of the DPP items. Each DPP item falls into one or more of the categories listed below. A brief menu of the DPP items included in Unit 14 follows.

N Number Sense A, C, F, H, J	**Computation** D–F, J, L	**Time** H	**Geometry** I
Math Facts A–C, G, K, M, O	**$ Money** E, F	**Measurement**	**Data** H, N, P

Practice and Assessment of the Division Facts

The DPP for this unit continues the systematic strategies-based approach to reviewing the division facts. This unit reviews the twos, fives, tens, and square numbers. The *Triangle Flash Cards* for these groups may be found in the *Unit Resource Guide* Generic Section and in the *Grade 4 Facts Resource Guide.* The cards for these groups were first distributed in the *Discovery Assignment Book,* following the Home Practice in Units 8, 10, and 11. A discussion of the flash cards and how to use them can be found in item B of the DPP. DPP items B, C, G, and K review the division facts. Two quizzes on the facts are provided in items M and O.

For more information about the distribution and assessment of the math facts, see the TIMS Tutor: *Math Facts* in the *Teacher Implementation Guide.* Also refer to the DPP guides in the *Unit Resource Guide* for Units 3 and 9.

Plant Growth Data Collection

In Unit 13 Lesson 5 students began the *Plant Growth* lab. In the Lesson Guide for the lab, we suggested planting the seeds on a Thursday or Friday. Regular data collection, at least three times a week, is suggested (e.g., Mondays, Wednesdays, and Fridays). To make the data collection a part of your class routine, you may wish to use the data collection as a replacement for some of the daily bits for this unit. (See Unit 13 Lesson 5 for more details about the *Plant Growth* lab.)

In addition to the data collection or on the days when measurements need not be taken, have students complete DPP items that review the division facts.

Students may solve the items individually, in groups, or as a class. The items may also be assigned for homework.

Student Questions	Teacher Notes

A) Guess My Number

I am a multiple of 2 and 3.

I am less than 63 but greater than 48.

I am not prime.

I am not a multiple of 10.

1. What number am I?

2. What clue above is redundant or unnecessary?

3. If I'm a multiple of 2 and 3, I must be a multiple of what other number?

TIMS Bit

1. 54

2. "I am not prime." Since the number is a multiple of 2 and 3, the number cannot be prime.

3. 6

Division Facts

With a partner, use your *Triangle Flash Cards* to quiz each other on the division facts for the 5s, 10s, 2s, and square numbers. One partner covers the corner with the number in a circle. This number will be the answer to a division fact, called the quotient. The second person uses the two uncovered numbers to solve a division fact.

Go through the cards again. This time the first person covers the number in the square and the second solves a division fact using the two uncovered numbers.

Each time through the cards, separate them into three piles: those facts you know and can answer quickly, those that you can figure out with a strategy, and those that you need to learn. Practice the last two piles again and then make a list of the facts you need to practice at home for homework.

Circle the facts you know and can answer quickly on your *Division Facts I Know* chart.

The flash cards for these groups of facts can be found in the *Unit Resource Guide* Generic Section and the *Grade 4 Facts Resource Guide.* They were distributed in Units 8, 10, and 11 in the *Discovery Assignment Book.* Students will need the flash cards to review all the facts again in Unit 16.

Students make a list of the facts they need to practice at home for homework as well as update their *Division Facts I Know* charts. In Part 1 of the Home Practice, students are reminded to bring home their *Triangle Flash Cards* to study.

Inform students when the two quizzes on the facts will be. These quizzes appear in items M and O.

Student Questions	Teacher Notes

C · More Division Facts

A. $90 \div 9 =$

B. $6 \div 3 =$

C. $9 \div 3 =$

D. $40 \div 10 =$

E. $20 \div 2 =$

F. $64 \div 8 =$

G. $8 \div 4 =$

H. $10 \div 2 =$

I. $36 \div 6 =$

J. $70 \div 7 =$

K. $10 \div 5 =$

L. $18 \div 9 =$

M. $16 \div 8 =$

N. $5 \div 5 =$

O. $50 \div 5 =$

P. $25 \div 5 =$

Q. $15 \div 3 =$

R. $4 \div 2 =$

TIMS Bit

A. 10   B. 2

C. 3   D. 4

E. 10   F. 8

G. 2   H. 5

I. 6   J. 10

K. 2   L. 2

M. 2   N. 1

O. 10   P. 5

Q. 5   R. 2

D · Division Practice

Solve the following using a paper-and-pencil method or mental math. Estimate to make sure your answers are reasonable.

1. A. $727 \div 6 =$

   B. $328 \div 9 =$

   C. $307 \div 4 =$

   D. $7435 \div 5 =$

   E. $1436 \div 4 =$

   F. $3005 \div 8 =$

2. Explain your estimation strategy for Question 1B.

TIMS Task

1. A. 121 R1

   B. 36 R4

   C. 76 R3

   D. 1487

   E. 359

   F. 375 R5

2. Possible strategy:
   $330 \div 10 = 33$.

Chances

Shannon, Roberto, and several friends went door to door selling 10¢ chances to a raffle that raised money for their youth center. They raised $325. How many chances did they sell?

TIMS Bit

3250 chances; Encourage students to share their strategies. Using a calculator, students may divide $325 by $0.10. Some students might do the problem in their heads using multiplication. Since 10 dimes are in one dollar, for every dollar raised 10 chances were sold— $10 \times 325 = 3250$.

 Lots of Money

How much change will you receive from a $10.00 bill if you spend the following amounts? Pretend you are at the store without your calculator or paper and pencil. See how many of the answers you can figure out in your head. What strategies did you use?

A. $5.60

B. $7.45

C. $1.97

D. $4.25

TIMS Task

1. A. $4.40; $5.60 to $6.00 is 40¢. The difference between $6 and $10 is $4. The change due is $4 + 40¢ or $4.40.

    B. $2.55; One possible strategy: 45¢ to 50¢ is a nickel. 50¢ more brings you up to $8. $8 to $10 is a difference of $2. $2 + 55¢ is $2.55.

    C. $8.03; $1.97 is close to $2. $10 − $2 = $8; $2 − $1.97 = $0.03; $8 + $0.03 = $8.03.

    D. $5.75; $4.25 + $5 = $9.25; $9.25 + $0.75 = $10; $5 + $0.75 = $5.75.

Student Questions	Teacher Notes

 Fact Families for × and ÷

The following four facts belong to the same fact family.

$4 \times 2 = 8$ $2 \times 4 = 8$
$8 \div 2 = 4$ $8 \div 4 = 2$

Solve each fact. Then, name the other facts that are in the same fact family.

A. $12 \div 2 =$ B. $6 \times 5 =$

C. $9 \times 9 =$ D. $60 \div 6 =$

E. $2 \times 7 =$ F. $20 \div 5 =$

G. $9 \times 5 =$ H. $8 \times 10 =$

I. $16 \div 4 =$ J. $49 \div 7 =$

K. $40 \div 8 =$ L. $8 \times 8 =$

M. $10 \times 10 =$ N. $5 \times 7 =$

TIMS Bit

Complete this item orally as a class. One student can solve the given fact and other students can name each of the other related facts.

A. 6; $12 \div 6 = 2$
    $6 \times 2 = 12$
    $2 \times 6 = 12$

B. 30; $5 \times 6 = 30$
    $30 \div 6 = 5$
    $30 \div 5 = 6$

C. 81
    $81 \div 9 = 9$

D. 10; $60 \div 10 = 6$
    $6 \times 10 = 60$
    $10 \times 6 = 60$

E. 14; $7 \times 2 = 14$
    $14 \div 7 = 2$
    $14 \div 2 = 7$

F. 4; $20 \div 4 = 5$
    $4 \times 5 = 20$
    $5 \times 4 = 20$

G. 45; $5 \times 9 = 45$
    $45 \div 5 = 9$
    $45 \div 9 = 5$

H. 80; $10 \times 8 = 80$
    $80 \div 8 = 10$
    $80 \div 10 = 8$

I. 4; $4 \times 4 = 16$

J. 7; $7 \times 7 = 49$

K. 5; $40 \div 5 = 8$
    $5 \times 8 = 40$
    $8 \times 5 = 40$

L. 64; $64 \div 8 = 8$

M. 100; $100 \div 10 = 10$

N. 35; $7 \times 5 = 35$
    $35 \div 7 = 5$
    $35 \div 5 = 7$

The 100-Meter Dash

The results of a 100-meter race are as follows. Instead of using names, participants were assigned numbers. Answer the following questions:

Runner	#253	#40	#685	#421	#89	#14	#26	#570
Time in seconds	13.6	15.1	14.9	14.8	13.8	14.4	15	10.4

1. In what order did the runners cross the finish line?

2. Most of the runners were fourth-graders. Which runner was most likely a professional athlete?

3. Use a calculator to find the average time for the race. (Find the mean.) Is your answer reasonable?

4. How much time passed between the times the first- and second-place winners crossed the finish line?

TIMS Challenge

1. #570, #253, #89, #14, #421, #685, #26, #40

2. #570

3. 14 seconds

4. 3.2 seconds

 Lines

1. List all pairs of lines that appear to be parallel in the drawing.

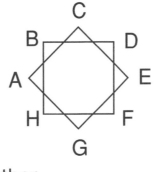

2. List the pairs of lines that appear to be perpendicular to each other.

TIMS Bit

1. $\overleftrightarrow{AC}$, and $\overleftrightarrow{GE}$; $\overleftrightarrow{CE}$ and $\overleftrightarrow{AG}$; $\overleftrightarrow{BD}$ and $\overleftrightarrow{FH}$; $\overleftrightarrow{BH}$ and $\overleftrightarrow{DF}$

2. $\overleftrightarrow{AC}$, and $\overleftrightarrow{CE}$; $\overleftrightarrow{CE}$ and $\overleftrightarrow{EG}$; $\overleftrightarrow{EG}$ and $\overleftrightarrow{AG}$; $\overleftrightarrow{AG}$ and $\overleftrightarrow{AC}$; $\overleftrightarrow{BD}$ and $\overleftrightarrow{DF}$; $\overleftrightarrow{DF}$ and $\overleftrightarrow{FH}$; $\overleftrightarrow{HF}$ and $\overleftrightarrow{BH}$; $\overleftrightarrow{BH}$ and $\overleftrightarrow{BD}$

Student Questions	Teacher Notes

 J **Adding and Subtracting**

Solve the following problems in your head.

1. A. $1700 + 400 =$

   B. $4300 - 400 =$

   C. $1450 + 350 =$

   D. $1658 - 500 =$

   E. $5033 + 9100 =$

   F. $2099 + 301 =$

2. Explain your strategy for Questions 1C and 1D.

TIMS Task

1. A. 2100   B. 3900
   C. 1800   D. 1158
   E. 14,133   F. 2400

2. Possible strategies are as follows.
   1C: 1450 + 50 = 1500, 1500 + 300 = 1800;
   1D: 58 − 0 = 58, 1600 − 500 = 1100, answer is 1158.

K **Still More Division Facts**

Complete the table using division. Use the number in the first column as your divisor. Write your answer (the quotient) in the empty boxes.

÷	10	20	30	40	50	100
2						
5						
10						

What patterns do you see?

TIMS Bit

÷	10	20	30	40	50	100
2	5	10	15	20	25	50
5	2	4	6	8	10	20
10	1	2	3	4	5	10

Student Questions	Teacher Notes

 Multiplication and Division Practice

Solve the following using paper-and-pencil methods or mental math. Estimate to make sure your answers are reasonable.

1. A. 23 × 64 =   B. 48 × 93 =

    C. 91 × 46 =   D. 57 × 70 =

    E. 173 ÷ 5 =   F. 2106 ÷ 6 =

    G. 3590 ÷ 7 =   H. 7853 ÷ 9 =

2. Explain your estimation strategy for Question 1B.

TIMS Task

1. A. 1472

    B. 4464

    C. 4186

    D. 3990

    E. 34 R3

    F. 351

    G. 512 R6

    I. 872 R5

2. Possible strategy:
    50 × 90 = 4500.

 Division Facts Quiz 1

A. 35 ÷ 7 =	B. 64 ÷ 8 =
C. 14 ÷ 2 =	D. 80 ÷ 8 =
E. 8 ÷ 4 =	F. 16 ÷ 4 =
G. 50 ÷ 10 =	H. 36 ÷ 6 =
I. 9 ÷ 3 =	J. 100 ÷ 10 =
K. 30 ÷ 5 =	L. 40 ÷ 4 =
M. 18 ÷ 9 =	N. 6 ÷ 2 =
O. 25 ÷ 5 =	P. 5 ÷ 5 =

TIMS Bit

This quiz is the first of two quizzes on the division facts for the 5s, 10s, 2s, and square numbers. Half of the facts are in this quiz and half appear in the second quiz in item O. We recommend 2 minutes for this quiz. Allow students to change pens after the time is up and complete the remaining problems in a different color.

After students take the quiz, have them update their *Division Facts I Know* charts.

Since students learned the division facts through work with fact families, it is likely that the student who answers 35 ÷ 7 correctly also knows the answer to 35 ÷ 5. To make sure, however, ask students to write a related division fact for each of the facts on the quiz (except the square numbers). A student who answers a given fact correctly and who also writes the correct related fact can circle both facts on the chart.

Student Questions	Teacher Notes

 Probability: Number Cubes

TIMS Task

Irma found a strange number cube. It had six faces but did not have the numbers 1 through 6 on it. It had the following numbers: 4, 4, 4, 5, 5, and 6.

1. $\frac{1}{6}$

2. $\frac{3}{6}$ or $\frac{1}{2}$

3. $\frac{2}{6}$ or $\frac{1}{3}$

4. $\frac{4}{6}$ or $\frac{2}{3}$

1. What is the probability that Irma will roll a 6?

2. What is the probability that Irma will roll a 4?

3. What is the probability that Irma will roll a 5?

4. What is the probability that Irma will roll an even number?

 Division Facts Quiz 2

TIMS Bit

A. $10 \div 1 =$	B. $40 \div 8 =$
C. $10 \div 5 =$	D. $49 \div 7 =$
E. $70 \div 7 =$	F. $16 \div 8 =$
G. $4 \div 2 =$	H. $15 \div 5 =$
I. $20 \div 5 =$	J. $81 \div 9 =$
K. $45 \div 9 =$	L. $30 \div 3 =$
M. $12 \div 6 =$	N. $60 \div 10 =$
O. $20 \div 2 =$	P. $90 \div 9 =$

This quiz is on the division facts for the 5s, 10s, 2s, and square numbers. Half of the facts are on this quiz. Half appear on the quiz in item M. We recommend 2 minutes for this quiz. Allow students to change pens after the time is up and complete the remaining problems in a different color.

After students take the quiz, have them update their *Division Facts I Know* charts.

It is likely that the student who answers 40 ÷ 8 correctly also knows 40 ÷ 5. To make sure, ask students to write the related division fact for each fact on the quiz (except the square numbers). A student who answers a given fact correctly and who also writes the given related division fact correctly can circle both facts on the chart.

Probability: Spinners

Draw a probability line on your paper. Each of the following statements has a letter in front of it. Use the letter to place the statement on the line correctly.

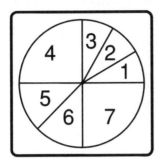

A. The probability of the spinner landing in Region 4.

B. The probability of the spinner landing in Region 4 or 7.

C. The probability of the spinner landing in Region 5.

D. The probability of the spinner landing in Region 2.

E. The probability of the spinner landing in Regions 1, 2, or 3.

F. The probability of the spinner landing in Region 8.

TIMS Challenge

```
0%    25%    50%    75%   100%
 +‑+‑+‑‑+‑‑‑‑‑‑+‑‑‑‑‑+‑‑‑‑‑+‑→
FDC  A E        B
```

A. $\frac{1}{4}$ or 25%

B. $\frac{1}{2}$ or 50%

C. $\frac{1}{8}$

D. $\frac{1}{12}$

E. $\frac{1}{4}$ or 25%

F. 0

Daily Practice and Problems:
Bit for Lesson 1

A. Guess My Number (URG p. 12)

I am a multiple of 2 and 3.

I am less than 63 but greater than 48.

I am not prime.

I am not a multiple of 10.

1. What number am I?

2. What clue above is redundant or unnecessary?

3. If I'm a multiple of 2 and 3, I must be a multiple of what other number?

DPP Task is on page 27. Suggestions for using the DPPs are on page 27.

LESSON GUIDE 1
Chance Discussions

Estimated
Class
Sessions:
1

Students explore concepts of chance by discussing the probability of various events. They help construct a "probability line" as a way of quantifying their ideas.

Key Content

- Defining probability.
- Representing probabilities on a number line.
- Connecting mathematics and real-world situations: estimating probabilities of real-world events.
- Expressing probabilities using qualitative terms: certain, likely, unlikely, impossible.

Key Vocabulary

certain
impossible
likely
probability
unlikely

Materials List

Print Materials for Students

	Math Facts and Daily Practice and Problems	Activity	Homework
Student Books — Student Guide		*Chance Discussions* Pages 384–385	*Chance Discussions* Homework Section Page 386
Discovery Assignment Book			Home Practice Part 1 Page 227
Teacher Resources — Facts Resource Guide	DPP Items 14A & 14B Use the *Triangle Flash Cards* for the *2s, 5s, 10s,* and *Square Numbers* to practice the division facts for these groups.		
Unit Resource Guide	DPP Items A–B Pages 12–13		
Generic Section			*Triangle Flash Cards: 2s, 5s, 10s,* and *Square Numbers,* 1 each per student (optional)

available on Teacher Resource CD

All Transparency Masters, Blackline Masters, and Assessment Blackline Masters in the Unit Resource Guide are on the Teacher Resource CD.

Supplies for Each Student Group

4 self-adhesive notes

Developing the Activity

Draw a horizontal line on the board about 2 meters long. Place a mark at the middle of the line. Ask students if they have ever heard the words "probability" or "chance." It should not come as a surprise if the words are unfamiliar. You could ask whether they have heard of the "chance of rain." Have the class generate a list of events which have no chance of happening, as well as a list of events which are certain to happen. Following are some ideas generated by a fourth-grade class:

Impossible
"Stuffed animals turning real."
"A car driving by itself."
"Aliens coming to the Earth."
"A picture changing after it was taken."
"Day and night in the exact same place
at the exact same second."

Certain
"I'm going to be at home on Saturday."
"We will get homework."
"A person will die."
"Seasons change."
"When you are born, you are a baby."

Students might not all agree on what is truly impossible. In addition, over time, an event that was once impossible may become possible. During the 1940s people would have said that it was impossible for a man to walk on the moon. Since 1969, we have known that it is possible. The study of robotics has made it possible for a car to drive by itself.

On the other hand, events that seem to be certain may, in fact, be less than certain. Although I plan to be at home on Saturday, something else may come up. Use terms such as very likely and very unlikely or almost impossible and almost certain to indicate a range of probability, particularly when the class is unable to reach consensus.

Use the line on the board to illustrate and compare the probability of events occurring. Elicit ideas for one word to describe something that cannot happen. They are likely to suggest "impossible," "cannot," or "never." Reach a consensus and label the left end of the line. Do the same brainstorming for a word to describe something that is certain to happen and label the right end of the line with this word.

Explain that mathematicians often use numbers to describe how likely events are to happen. A "0" is used to denote when something is impossible. We say that it has a "zero probability of happening."

Label the left end of the line with a zero. A "1" is used to denote certainty. Label the right end of the line with a "1." A **probability** is a measure of how likely an event is to happen. Probabilities can be expressed as fractions, decimals, or percents. Students are probably familiar with hearing something like, "It's 100% certain." Since 100% means "one whole," a probability of 1 is the same as a probability of 100%. To show this, label the left and right ends of the line with 0% and 100%, respectively, as in Figure 9.

Now, direct attention to the center of the line. Ask:

- *This point is exactly halfway between what two points?* (0 and 1 or 0% and 100%)

- *What are two different labels for this point?* ($\frac{1}{2}$ and 50%)

- *What does this mean on our probability line?* (An event with 50% probability has an equal probability of happening or not happening.)

The last step in setting up the probability line is to discuss that broad area between 0 and 1 known as "maybe." Ask:

- *Where would we mark the probability of an event on the line that we are pretty sure will happen but not totally sure?* (between 50% and 100%)

- *Give an example.* (I'll go to sleep at my regular time tonight.)

- *Where would we mark an event that we are pretty sure will not happen, but not totally sure?* (between 0% and 50%)

- *Give an example.* (I'll stay awake all night tonight.)

Discuss that the closer the probability is to 0 or 0%, the less likely the event is to happen; the closer the probability is to 1 or 100%, the more likely the event is to happen. For most events, we will not know an exact probability. But it is possible to compare some events. Ask:

- *Where would we mark the probability that one of the students in this class will grow to be over 7 feet tall?* (near 0 or 0%)

- *Should we place the mark at exactly 0? Why or why not?* (No, because there is a small chance that someone in the class actually would grow to be 7 feet tall. There are people who have grown this tall. We won't know for sure until all the students have reached their full height.)

- *Where would we mark the probability that one of the students in this class will grow to be over 6 feet tall?* (near 1 or 100%)

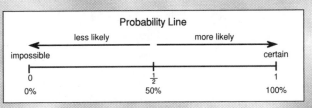

Figure 9: *A probability line*

Chance Discussions

Sure Things?

Some things are **impossible.**
They cannot happen. What is
impossible about the picture below?

Other things are **unlikely.** They can happen,
but they won't happen very often. It is unlikely
that you will grow to a height of 7 feet.

Chance Discussions

Student Guide - Page 384

Still other things are **likely.** They
probably will happen, but they might
not. It is likely that you will grow to a
height of at least 4 feet.

Finally, some things are **certain.** They
are sure to happen. It is certain that you
will grow to a height of more than 1 inch.

Probability is a measure of how likely
things are to happen. Events that are
impossible have probability 0%. Events
that are certain have probability 100%.
The larger the probability, the more
likely an event is to happen.

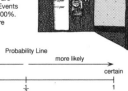

Probability Line

less likely   more likely

impossible   certain
├──────────┼──────────┤
0   1/2   1
0%   50%   100%

Draw a probability line like the one above. Where would each of the following
events appear on the line? Use the letters to place each event on the line.

   A. It will be cold tomorrow at the South Pole.
   B. There is fruit in your refrigerator at home.
   C. Elvis Presley will be the next President of the United States.
   D. You will receive mail today.
   E. The Chicago Cubs will win the Super Bowl next year.
   F. You will fly to the moon tomorrow.
   G. A penny will show heads when flipped once.
   H. When flipping a penny, you get heads ten times in a row.
   I. Monday will follow Sunday.
   J. You will have homework tonight.
   K. A newborn baby will be a girl.
   L. It is going to snow tomorrow.
   M. You will be sick tomorrow.

Chance Discussions

Student Guide - Page 385

- *Should we place this mark at exactly 1 or 100%?
  Why or why not?* (No, because there is a small
  chance that no one would grow to be over 6 feet
  tall. It is not unusual for a person's full height to
  be less than 6 feet, although it would be unlikely
  that no one reached that height.)

- *Where should we mark the probability that
  one of the students will grow to be over
  5 feet tall? 9 feet tall? 12 feet tall?*

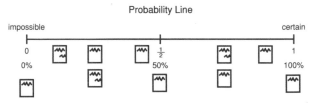

Probability Line

impossible   certain

0   1/2   1
0%   50%   100%

Figure 10: *Students record events on self-adhesive
notes and post them beneath the probability line.*

Have students work in groups of four to make a list
of four events to be placed somewhere on the line.
They might think of events such as, "I will go to
sleep before 10 P.M. tonight," "I will have a peanut
butter sandwich for lunch tomorrow," "My favorite
team will win the playoffs this year," "It will rain
tomorrow," "The phone will ring during supper at
my house tonight." Ask them to record each event on
a self-adhesive note, make a rough estimate of its
likelihood, and place it on the line accordingly.

Ask each group to share their thinking with the
class. Allow students to discuss the placement of the
items and to post their ideas beneath the probability
line, as in Figure 10.

After this introduction to probability, use the *Chance
Discussions* Activity Pages from the *Student Guide*
to conclude this lesson.

Journal Prompt

Why do you think probability is an important idea?

Suggestions for Teaching the Lesson

Math Facts

- DPP Bit A requires students to use their knowledge of math facts to solve a riddle. Task B reminds students to use their *Triangle Flash Cards* to practice the division math facts.
- Part 1 of the Home Practice reminds students to practice division facts using their *Triangle Flash Cards*.

Homework and Practice

In the Homework section of the *Chance Discussions* Activity Pages, students find examples of events in each of the probability categories: 0%, not likely, 50%, likely, and 100%.

Daily Practice and Problems: Task for Lesson 1

B. Task: Division Facts (URG p. 13)

With a partner, use your *Triangle Flash Cards* to quiz each other on the division facts for the 5s, 10s, 2s, and square numbers. One partner covers the corner with the number in a circle. This number will be the answer to a division fact, called the quotient. The second person uses the two uncovered numbers to solve a division fact.

Go through the cards again. This time the first person covers the number in the square and the second solves a division fact using the two uncovered numbers.

Each time through the cards, separate them into three piles: those facts you know and can answer quickly, those that you can figure out with a strategy, and those that you need to learn. Practice the last two piles again and then make a list of the facts you need to practice at home for homework.

Circle the facts you know and can answer quickly on your *Division Facts I Know* chart.

Name _____ Date _____

Unit 14: Home Practice

Part 1 *Triangle Flash Cards: 5s, 10s, 2s,* and **Square Numbers**

Study for the quizzes on the division facts. Take home your *Triangle Flash Cards* and your list of facts you need to study.

Here's how to use the flash cards. Ask a family member to choose one flash card at a time. Your partner should cover the corner with the circle. This number will be the answer to a division fact, called the quotient. Use the two uncovered numbers to solve a division fact. Then have your partner go through the cards covering the corner with a square. Use the two uncovered numbers to solve a division fact.

Your teacher will tell you when the quiz on the facts will be. Remember to study only those facts you cannot answer correctly and quickly.

Part 2 **School Supplies**
The school store sells school supplies. The prices for notebooks, pencils, markers, and folders are shown.

spiral notebook	pencils	markers	folders
$0.39	4 for $1.00	$2.98	10 for $1.00

Jessie bought 4 spiral notebooks, 1 set of markers, 8 folders, and 10 pencils.

Jacob bought 5 spiral notebooks, 1 set of markers, 10 folders, and 5 pencils.

Choose an appropriate method to solve each of the following problems. For each question, you may choose to use paper and pencil, mental math, or a calculator. Be prepared to explain how you solved each problem. Use a separate sheet of paper to show your work.

1. Figure out the exact cost of each student's supplies.
2. Whose supplies cost the most?
3. What is the difference in price between the two students' supplies?
4. Choose one of the students' lists and explain how you figured out the total. What was the hardest part of the problem? Why?

Discovery Assignment Book - Page 227

Homework

The letters A, B, C, D, and E on the probability line below represent five different probability categories: 0%, not likely, 50%, likely, and 100%. Look around your home. For each letter on the line, give an example of an event with that probability. Record your examples on a separate sheet of paper.

Probability Line

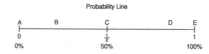

Student Guide - Page 386

AT A GLANCE

Math Facts and Daily Practice and Problems

DPP Bit A uses math facts to solve a puzzle. Task B reminds students to use the *Triangle Flash Cards* to study division facts.

Developing the Activity

1. Draw a line on the blackboard about 2 meters long. Label it the Probability Line.
2. Students suggest events that are certain to happen and those that are impossible.
3. Mark the two ends of the line with 0, 0% and 1, 100%.
4. Work together to place a variety of events on the Probability Line.
5. Use the *Chance Discussions* Activity Pages from the *Student Guide* to conclude the lesson.

Homework

1. Assign the Homework section on the *Chance Discussions* Activity Pages for homework.
2. Assign Part 1 of the Home Practice.

Notes:

Answer Key • Lesson 1: Chance Discussions

Student Guide

Questions A–M (SG p. 385)

A.–M. Answers will vary. One possible completed probability line: The placement of B, D, J, M, and L on the probability line will vary.

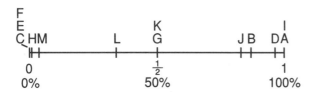

Homework (SG p. 386)

Answers will vary.

*Answers and/or discussion are included in the Lesson Guide.

**Answers for all the Home Practice in the *Discovery Assignment Book* are at the end of the unit.

LESSON GUIDE

Bean Counter's Game

Estimated Class Sessions: 1

Students continue their exploration of probability by playing a game with a number cube. This game introduces students to the probabilities involved when rolling a number cube and prepares students for the lab, *Rolling a Number Cube,* in Lesson 3.

Key Content

* Making predictions about the outcomes of a random process: rolling one number cube.
* Exploring situations that have outcomes that are equally likely.

Key Vocabulary

number cube

Daily Practice and Problems: Bit for Lesson 2

C. More Division Facts (URG p. 14)

A. $90 \div 9 =$ B. $6 \div 3 =$

C. $9 \div 3 =$ D. $40 \div 10 =$

E. $20 \div 2 =$ F. $64 \div 8 =$

G. $8 \div 4 =$ H. $10 \div 2 =$

I. $36 \div 6 =$ J. $70 \div 7 =$

K. $10 \div 5 =$ L. $18 \div 9 =$

M. $16 \div 8 =$ N. $5 \div 5 =$

O. $50 \div 5 =$ P. $25 \div 5 =$

Q. $15 \div 3 =$ R. $4 \div 2 =$

DPP Task is on page 32. Suggestions for using the DPPs are on page 32.

Materials List

Print Materials for Students

	Math Facts and Daily Practice and Problems	Game	Homework
Student Books — Student Guide		Bean Counter's Game Page 387	
Student Books — Discovery Assignment Book			Home Practice Parts 4 & 5 Page 229
Teacher Resources — Facts Resource Guide	DPP Item 14C		
Teacher Resources — Unit Resource Guide	DPP Items C–D Page 14		

available on Teacher Resource CD

All Transparency Masters, Blackline Masters, and Assessment Blackline Masters in the Unit Resource Guide are on the Teacher Resource CD.

Supplies for Each Student Group

scratch paper
number cube
beans, small tokens, or centimeter connecting cubes to be used as tokens, 12 per student

Developing the Game

Introduce *Bean Counter's Game,* found in the *Student Guide.* In the game, students distribute 12 beans above the numbers (one through six) on a number line in any way they choose. They then remove the beans one at a time, according to the faces that show when a number cube is rolled. The student who removes all of his or her beans first is the winner. Because each number is equally likely to come up on a roll, students who spread their beans out equally above all the numbers are more likely to win than students who place many beans on only a few numbers. Students may not realize this strategy at first; let them discover it on their own.

Have two students come to the overhead to demonstrate the game for the class. Then allow time for the rest of the class to play in groups of two or three. As students play the game, circulate about the room and note students' conversations about their strategies.

After the class has played the game, start a discussion. Ask the winners if they employed any particular strategies, and what they were. Ask:

- *If you play again, how would you change the bean placement?*

Playing the game sets the stage for Lesson 3 *Rolling A Number Cube.* Further discussion of the game will take place as part of Lesson 3.

Journal Prompt

Describe a winning strategy for the game. Explain why you chose that strategy.

TIMS Tip

Instead of using beans or tokens, you can have students keep score in a different way. They can draw circles above the numbers on their number lines. When the number cube is rolled, students can cross out the appropriate circle.

Bean Counter's Game

This is a game for 2–3 players. The object of this game is to be the first player to eliminate all twelve beans from his or her number line.

Materials

scratch paper
twelve beans or game markers per player
one number cube

Before Playing the Game

Each player first draws a line on a piece of scratch paper and then draws the six faces of a number cube as shown.

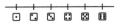

Rules for the Game

1. Each player distributes twelve beans any way he or she chooses above the drawings of the faces. Here are two examples of ways to spread the beans on the number line.

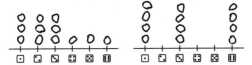

2. Decide which player will roll the number cube for the whole game. That player rolls the cube and reads the number that is face up.

3. For each roll, each player removes a bean above the matching face on the number line. If there is no bean above that face, the player removes nothing.

4. Continue rolling the number cube and removing the beans. The first player to remove all the beans from his or her board is the winner.

Bean Counter's Game   SG · Grade 4 · Unit 14 · Lesson 2 387

Student Guide - Page 387

Daily Practice and Problems: Task for Lesson 2

D. Task: Division Practice (URG p. 14)

Solve the following using a paper-and-pencil method or mental math. Estimate to make sure your answers are reasonable.

1. A. $727 \div 6 =$

    B. $328 \div 9 =$

    C. $307 \div 4 =$

    D. $7435 \div 5 =$

    E. $1436 \div 4 =$

    F. $3005 \div 8 =$

2. Explain your estimation strategy for Question 1B.

Suggestions for Teaching the Lesson

Math Facts

DPP Bit C provides division facts practice.

Homework and Practice

- The game can be sent home to be played with family members.
- DPP Task D provides computation practice with division.
- Assign Parts 4 and 5 of the Home Practice in the *Discovery Assignment Book.* Part 4 provides practice representing the probability of events on a Probability Line. Part 5 asks students to look for patterns in multiplying by multiples of 10.

Answers for Parts 4 and 5 of the Home Practice can be found in the Answer Key at the end of this lesson and at the end of this unit.

Extension

Students can begin the game with 18 beans.

Name _____ Date _____

Part 4 Probability Lines
Use letters to place the following events on the probability line below.

Probability Line

impossible   certain
|———————|———————|
0              $\frac{1}{2}$ 1
0%   50%   100%

A. Romesh will be the next president of the United States.
B. A spinner is evenly divided into four colors: red, blue, green, and yellow. In one spin, it will land on green.
C. You will travel to Europe next year.
D. Martians will invade the planet this afternoon.
E. A coin flip will land on heads.
F. It will rain tomorrow.
G. There will be seven days in next week.
H. The sidewalk in front of the school is concrete.
I. A dog will have kittens.
J. You will win the lottery today.

Part 5 The Power of 10
Use paper and pencil, not a calculator, for these problems.

A. What patterns do you notice in the problems?
B. What pattern do you think you will see in the answers?

C.	832	D.	832	E.	832	F.	832
	$\times 6$		$\times 60$		$\times 600$		$\times 6000$

G.	759	H.	759	I.	759	J.	759
	$\times 6$		$\times 60$		$\times 600$		$\times 6000$

K. Arrange your answers from smallest to largest.

Discovery Assignment Book - Page 229

AT A GLANCE

Math Facts and Daily Practice and Problems

DPP Bit C reviews division facts for the 2s, 5s, 10s, and square numbers. Task D reviews division computation.

Developing the Game

1. Introduce *Bean Counter's Game* by having two students demonstrate it at the overhead for the class using the directions in the *Student Guide.*
2. Allow time for the entire class to play.
3. Talk about the strategies which emerged from the play.

Homework

1. Students can play the game at home with family members.
2. Assign Home Practice Parts 4 and 5.

Notes:

Discovery Assignment Book

**Home Practice (DAB p. 229)

Part 4. Probability Lines

Questions A–J

The placement of C, F, and H on the probability line will vary.

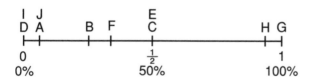

Part 5. The Power of 10

Questions A–K

A. Answers may vary. The second factor in each problem increases by a factor of 10 each time, so there is one more zero in each of these numbers.

B. The answers will also increase by a factor of 10 each time, so there will be one more zero in each answer.

C. 4992

D. 49,920

E. 499,200

F. 4,992,000

G. 4554

H. 45,540

I. 455,400

J. 4,554,000

K. 4554; 4992; 45,540; 49,920; 455,400; 499,200; 4,554,000; 4,992,000

---

*Answers and/or discussion are included in the Lesson Guide.

**Answers for all the Home *Practice in the Discovery Assignment Book* are at the end of the unit.

Daily Practice and Problems: Bits for Lesson 3

E. Chances (URG p. 15)

Shannon, Roberto, and several friends went door to door selling 10¢ chances to a raffle that raised money for their youth center. They raised $325. How many chances did they sell?

G. Fact Families for × and ÷
(URG p. 16)

The following four facts belong to the same fact family.

$$4 \times 2 = 8 \qquad 2 \times 4 = 8$$
$$8 \div 2 = 4 \qquad 8 \div 4 = 2$$

Solve each fact. Then, name the other facts that are in the same fact family.

A. $12 \div 2 =$ B. $6 \times 5 =$

C. $9 \times 9 =$ D. $60 \div 6 =$

E. $2 \times 7 =$ F. $20 \div 5 =$

G. $9 \times 5 =$ H. $8 \times 10 =$

I. $16 \div 4 =$ J. $49 \div 7 =$

K. $40 \div 8 =$ L. $8 \times 8 =$

M. $10 \times 10 =$ N. $5 \times 7 =$

DPP Task and Challenge are on page 41. Suggestions for using the DPPs are on page 40.

LESSON GUIDE 3

Rolling a Number Cube

Estimated Class Sessions: 2

Students investigate the outcome of a random process by rolling a number cube 60 times and analyzing the results. By pooling their data with other groups, students are able to see that large numbers of events produce results that are closer to the predicted results. A quiz on the probabilities of rolling a number cube is included with this lesson.

Key Content

- Exploring situations that have outcomes that are equally likely.
- Collecting and analyzing data from a random process.
- Making predictions about the outcome of a random process: rolling one number cube.
- Identifying patterns that emerge as the number of random events increases.
- Finding probabilities involved in rolling a number cube.
- Using probabilities to make predictions.
- Expressing probabilities as fractions.
- Comparing probabilities to real-world data: rolling one number cube.
- Making and interpreting bar graphs.
- Collecting, organizing, graphing, and analyzing data.

Key Vocabulary

fair number cube
probability

Curriculum Sequence

Before This Unit

Numerical Data. In Grade 3 Unit 1 students collected numerical data, represented the data in graphs, and made predictions using their results. In fourth grade, they completed similar investigations in Unit 1 Lesson 2 *Getting to Know Room 204 A Little Better* and in the *TV Survey* in Unit 13 Lesson 1.

Materials List

Print Materials for Students

		Math Facts and Daily Practice and Problems	Lab	Homework	Written Assessment
Student Books	**Student Guide**		*Rolling a Number Cube* Pages 388–391		
	Discovery Assignment Book			Home Practice Part 3 Page 228	
Teacher Resources	**Facts Resource Guide**	DPP Item 14G			
	Unit Resource Guide	DPP Items E–H Pages 15–17			*Check-up* Page 44, 1 per student
	Generic Section		*Centimeter Graph Paper,* 2 per student and *Three-column Data Table,* 1 per student pair		

available on Teacher Resource CD

All Transparency Masters, Blackline Masters, and Assessment Blackline Masters in the Unit Resource Guide are on the Teacher Resource CD.

Supplies for Each Student Pair

number cube
small paper cup, for rolling number cubes, optional
calculators

Materials for the Teacher

Number Cube Rolls: Class Data Table Transparency Master (Unit Resource Guide) Page 43
Observational Assessment Record (Unit Resource Guide, Pages 9–10 and Teacher Resource CD)

Rolling a Number Cube

In this lab, you and a partner will study what happens when a number cube is rolled many times. The main variables are *F*, the faces on the cube, and *T*, the number of times each face comes up.

1. Which variable is the manipulated variable?
2. Which variable is the responding variable?

 Collect

3. With your partner, roll the number cube 60 times. Tally the number of times each face comes up using a table like this:

Group's Data Table

F Face	T Number of Times Face Appeared	
	Tallies	Total
⚀		
⚁		
⚂		
⚃		
⚄		
⚅		

Group Grand Total _____

388 SG · Grade 4 · Unit 14 · Lesson 3   Rolling a Number Cube

Student Guide - Page 388

 Graph

4. **A.** Make a bar graph of your results.
   B. Describe your graph. For example, what can you say about the heights of the bars?

5. Combine your data with other groups to get data from the class. Record the class data on a table like this:

Class's Data Table

F Face	T Total Number of Times Face Appeared
⚀	
⚁	
⚂	
⚃	
⚄	
⚅	

Class Grand Total _____

6. **A.** Make a bar graph of the class data.
   B. Describe the class graph. What can you say about the heights of the bars?
   C. How is your graph of the class data different from your 60-roll group graph? Compare their shapes.

Rolling a Number Cube   SG · Grade 4 · Unit 14 · Lesson 3 389

Student Guide - Page 389

Developing the Lab

This lab follows the *Bean Counter's Game*. Explain to students that they are going to complete a lab which will address the issue of a probable winning strategy for the game. They will investigate whether a pattern emerges when a number cube is rolled many times.

Part 1. Collecting the Data

Explain to students that they will work with a partner to roll a number cube 60 times and record the results.

Before collecting data, students work with their partners to answer *Questions 1–2* on the *Rolling a Number Cube* Lab Pages in the *Student Guide*, which ask about the manipulated and responding variables. The manipulated variable is the variable whose values are known before the experiment begins. We can always put the values of the manipulated variable into the table *before* we begin to gather data. In this experiment, the manipulated variable is *F*, the faces on the number cube. We know before the experiment that its values are the faces on the cube: ⚀, ⚁, ⚂, ⚃, ⚄, and ⚅. The responding variable is the number of times (*T*) each face comes up. This is the variable whose values we learn by doing the experiment.

Next, have students collect the data *(Question 3)* by rolling their number cubes 60 times and tallying their results. Sometimes, students don't realize they have reached 60 rolls and they just keep on rolling and tallying. It is then a problem to know which tallies to erase. Ask for suggestions about how to keep track of the number of rolls. One way is to make 60 marks on a piece of paper and cross one out each time you roll. Another way is to record the raw data, that is, to record the face that shows on each of the 60 rolls, as shown in Figure 11. Then, students can either tally or simply write the number of times each face appears in the data table, as in Figure 12. Students may develop other strategies.

After the groups have completed the data collection, have each student make a bar graph of their data *(Question 4)*. After groups have shared their graphs with the class, ask students to describe the graphs. Ask:

• *Which groups had the "one" face appear most often?*

• *Which groups had the "two" face appear most often? etc.*

The graph of the sample data for one group (Figure 13) shows that one and five appeared most often, but students should see that different groups had differing results.

Raw Data

Roll	Face	Roll	Face
1	6	31	6
2	1	32	3
3	5	33	3
4	4	34	5
5	5	35	1
6	4	36	2
7	2	37	3
8	2	38	6
9	5	39	1
10	1	40	5
11	1	41	1
12	6	42	2
13	3	43	1
14	2	44	6
15	3	45	5
16	6	46	3
17	3	47	3
18	1	48	1
19	5	49	5
20	5	50	5
21	6	51	3
22	2	52	2
23	1	53	4
24	1	54	4
25	1	55	1
26	6	56	3
27	2	57	5
28	4	58	4
29	5	59	3
30	3	60	5

Figure 11: *Sample raw data with face showing on each roll*

F Face	T Number of Times Face Appeared	
	Tallies	**Total**
⚀	ЖГ ЖГ III	13
⚁	ЖГ III	8
⚂	ЖГ ЖГ II	12
⚃	ЖГ I	6
⚄	ЖГ ЖГ III	13
⚅	ЖГ III	8

Grand Total ___60___

Figure 12: *Sample 60-roll data table*

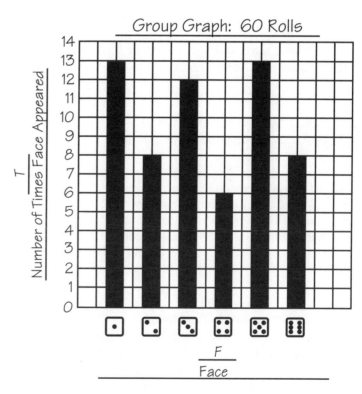

Figure 13: *Graph of 60-roll data*

Number Cube Rolls: Class Data Table

F Face	*T* Number of Times Face Appeared by Group										
	Gr. 1	Gr. 2	Gr. 3	Gr. 4	Gr. 5	Gr. 6	Gr. 7	Gr. 8	Gr. 9	Gr. 10	Total
⚀	9	5	8	10	10	14	10	8	17	8	99
⚁	11	11	10	6	8	10	7	6	6	15	90
⚂	13	11	3	13	15	8	12	7	7	10	99
⚃	12	9	14	8	10	10	10	12	12	12	109
⚄	8	17	11	8	10	6	9	13	12	8	102
⚅	7	7	14	15	7	12	12	14	6	7	101

Grand Total 600

Figure 14: *Sample class data table*

Next, pool data from several groups to get results for many rolls *(Question 5).* To do this, have each set of partners record their results on the blackboard or on the *Number Cube Rolls: Class Data Table* Transparency Master from the *Unit Resource Guide.* Students can then use calculators to find the total number of times each face appeared.

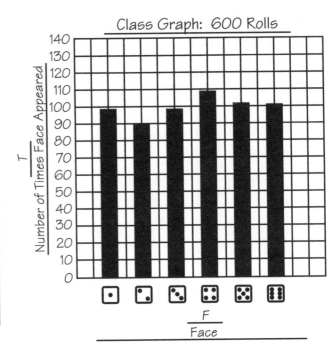

Figure 15: *Graph of class data*

TIMS Tip

We recommend pooling data from 10 groups, providing a total of 600 rolls. This is a nice number to work with. In questions such as *Question 7,* students will need to compute one sixth of the total number of rolls and finding one sixth of 600 will not be too difficult for them. You could pool the data from all the groups instead of just 10, but you should then discuss with the students methods for finding one sixth of the total. Students can use calculators to divide the total by six.

Have each student make a graph of the class data *(Question 6).* Before they begin, remind them to think about how to scale the vertical axis so all their data will fit. For a larger number of rolls, the height of the bars should be more even. This "evening out" is a consequence of the Law of Large Numbers. (See the Background for an explanation of the Law of Large Numbers.) A sample class graph is shown in Figure 15.

TIMS Tip

Save the *Number Cube Rolls: Class Data Table* Transparency Master after it has been filled in. You will use it in Lesson 4 *From Number Cubes to Spinners.* Students should also save their class graphs for use in Lesson 4. They are asked to compare their graphs of data collected with number cubes to data collected with spinners.

Questions 7–8 explore the idea of a fair number cube. A number cube is **fair** if all the faces are equally likely. Students can divide the total number of class rolls by 6 to get the number of times each face would come up if each came up an equal number of times. The faces probably didn't come up exactly the same number of times, but variations due to chance should be expected. For example, if the class rolled the number cubes a total number of 600 times, we would expect each face to show *about* 100 times *(Question 7A)*. The bars on the graph for 600 rolls (Figure 15) are much closer to being even than the bars on the graph for 60 rolls (Figure 13). Therefore, the data suggest that the number cubes used to collect this data are fair, since each face came up about 100 times *(Question 7B)*.

Content Note

Fair Number Cubes. Technically, to be able to say that all the number cubes used by the class are fair, each cube should be rolled a large number of times. However, we simplify the data collection by aggregating the data.

Part 2. The Lab and the Game

Have students think again about the *Bean Counter's Game* from Lesson 2. Based on their work in the lab, ask for ideas as to strategies for winning the game *(Question 9)*. Some might suggest evenly distributing the beans across the number line. This would be the best strategy in the long run, if the game is played many times. However, because of random variations, it might not always be the winning strategy. (Of course, if both players use this strategy, neither player has an advantage.) It might also be interesting to talk about distributions which would more likely cause you to lose (e.g., putting all the beans on one number).

Part 3. Number Cubes and Probability

The Number Cubes and Probability section in the *Student Guide* involves quantitative probabilities. Remind students that a number cube has six possible outcomes—the numbers 1, 2, 3, 4, 5, and 6. Since each face is equally likely to come up, the probability of any one face coming up is 1 out of 6 chances, or $\frac{1}{6}$. If you have erased it, redraw the Probability Line from Lesson 1. Ask the following questions:

- *Where would you place the probability of a 2 appearing when the cube is rolled?* (In the "less likely" area) *What is the probability of rolling a 2?* (One chance in six, or $\frac{1}{6}$) *Why?*

- *Is the probability of rolling a 5 more or less than 50%?* (Less) *What is the probability of rolling a 5?* (One chance in six, or $\frac{1}{6}$)

Occasionally, number cubes come from the factory poorly balanced. If you find that one face came up quite a bit more often than the others, you might suspect that the cubes you are using are not fair. You can ask interested students to repeat the experiment to see whether that same number came up more often again the second time.

7. A number cube is **fair** if each face is equally likely to come up.
   A. What is the total number of times your class rolled the number cubes? About how many times would you expect each face to come up if each face is equally likely?
   B. Look at your class data table and graph. In general, does the data show that your class used fair number cubes? Why or why not?

8. Suppose a number cube was rolled 1000 times and a 6 came up 500 times. Do you think it is a fair cube? Why or why not?

9. Think about the *Bean Counter's Game* in Lesson 2. Based on the results of this lab, describe a winning strategy for the game.

Number Cubes and Probability

Sometimes we can only estimate the probability of an event; we can say that the event is likely or unlikely, but we don't know its probability exactly. However, sometimes we can find the probability exactly.

For example, we can find the **probability** of rolling a particular face of a number cube. Since a normal number cube has six faces and only one of those faces is ⚁, there is just one chance out of six that ⚁ will show when the number cube is rolled. The probability of rolling ⚁ with a fair number cube is $\frac{1}{6}$. This means we can expect ⚁ to show about $\frac{1}{6}$ of the time.

What is the probability of rolling a number greater than 4? Two out of the six possible faces are greater than 4, namely 5 and 6. Therefore, the probability is $\frac{2}{6}$. If we rolled a number cube 600 times, we would expect to get a number greater than 4 about 200 times, since 200 is $\frac{2}{6}$ (or $\frac{1}{3}$) of 600.

10. Probability predicts that each face will come up *about* $\frac{1}{6}$ of the time when a number cube is rolled.
    A. Did this happen in your group's 60-roll data?
    B. Did this happen in your class's data?

Student Guide - Page 390

Content Note

Probability. The **probability** of an event occurring is equal to the number of favorable outcomes divided by the total number of possible outcomes.

Probability of an event = number of favorable outcomes/number of possible outcomes.

For example, the probability of rolling an odd number when rolling one number cube is $\frac{3}{6}$ or $\frac{1}{2}$.

$$\frac{3}{6} = \frac{\text{number of favorable outcomes (1, 3, 5)}}{\text{number of possible outcomes (1, 2, 3, 4, 5, 6)}}$$

Another example: If one letter of the alphabet is chosen at random, the probability of choosing a vowel is $\frac{5}{26}$.

$$\frac{5}{26} = \frac{\text{number of favorable outcomes (a, e, i, o, u)}}{\text{number of possible outcomes (26 total letters)}}$$

11. Probability predicts that a number greater than 4 (a 5 or a 6) will come up $\frac{1}{3}$ ($\frac{2}{6}$) of the time when a number cube is rolled. Does your class's data agree with this?

Answer the following questions about rolling a number cube.

12. A. What is the probability of rolling a 4? (Express your answer as a fraction.)
    B. Where would you place your answer to 12A on a probability line, nearer "1" or nearer "0"?

13. A. What are the odd numbers on the cube?
    B. What is the probability of rolling an odd number? (Express your answer as a fraction.) Explain your thinking.

14. A. What is the probability of rolling a number less than 3? (Express as a fraction.)
    B. On the probability line, would you place your answer to 14A closer to 0%, 50%, or 100%?

15. A. If Jessie rolls a 3 with a fair number cube, which of the following describes the probability of rolling a 3 on her next roll: (a) a little less than $\frac{1}{6}$, (b) equal to $\frac{1}{6}$, or (c) a little more than $\frac{1}{6}$?
    B. Why do you think so?

16. If you rolled a number cube 1200 times, about how many fives do you think would come up? Why do you think so?

Rolling a Number Cube   SG · Grade 4 · Unit 14 · Lesson 3 391

Student Guide - Page 391

Journal Prompt

What have you learned about probability and a number cube?

- *What is the probability of rolling a 7?* (Zero)
- *What is the probability of rolling a whole number between 0 and 7?* (100%)
- *What is the probability of rolling an even number?* There are 3 chances—faces 2, 4, and 6—out of 6 possible outcomes. The probability of rolling an even number is 3 out of 6 or the fraction $\frac{3}{6}$ or $\frac{1}{2}$.)
- *What is the probability of getting "heads" when flipping a coin?* (Since 1 of the 2 faces on a coin is a head, the probability of heads showing is $\frac{1}{2}$.)

Have students read the Number Cubes and Probability section of the *Rolling a Number Cube* Lab Pages in the *Student Guide*. **Questions 10–11** ask students to compare the results of their experiments with the probabilities. **Questions 12–16** ask them to compute various probabilities. **Question 15** asks about the probability of rolling a 3 immediately after a 3 has shown on the number cube. A common misconception (see the Law of Large Numbers in the Background) causes many people to believe that the probability decreases, or that a 3 is less likely to appear, after rolling one 3. On the contrary, the probability of rolling a 3 remains the same—$\frac{1}{6}$. Your students can verify this fact by completing the Extension activity described later in this Lesson Guide.

Suggestions for Teaching the Lesson

Math Facts

Bit G provides practice with division facts using fact families.

Homework and Practice

- *Questions 12–16* in the *Student Guide* can be used as homework.
- DPP Bit E is a word problem in which students choose which tool or method to use to perform a computation. Task F is mental math practice. Challenge H provides practice with decimals and data analysis.
- Remind students to study the division facts for the fives, tens, twos, and square numbers using their *Triangle Flash Cards*.
- Assign Home Practice Part 3, Multiplication and Division Practice, in the *Discovery Assignment Book*.

Answers for Part 3 of the Home Practice can be found in the Answer Key at the end of this lesson and at the end of this unit.

Assessment

- The *Check-up* Assessment Page in the *Unit Resource Guide* provides information to help you evaluate your students' understanding of the concepts in this lab.

- Document students' abilities to express probabilities as fractions and to make and interpret bar graphs on the *Observational Assessment Record.*

Extension

The class can do a project to determine whether a 3 is more or less likely to come up immediately after rolling a 3. Direct students to roll a number cube until a 3 comes up. Then, have them roll again and record the face that appears. Gather data from the entire class to show that the probability of rolling a second 3 is just what it always was—$\frac{1}{6}$.

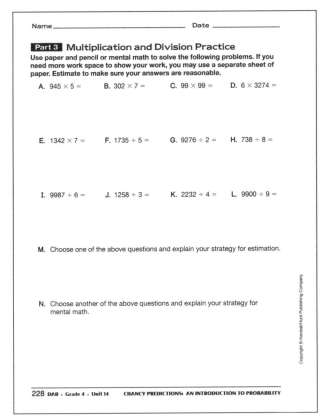

Discovery Assignment Book - Page 228

Daily Practice and Problems: Task and Challenge for Lesson 3

F. Task: Lots of Money

(URG p. 15)

How much change will you receive from a $10.00 bill if you spend the following amounts? Pretend you are at the store without your calculator or paper and pencil. See how many of the answers you can figure out in your head. What strategies did you use?

A. $5.60

B. $7.45

C. $1.97

D. $4.25

H. Challenge: The 100-Meter

Dash (URG p. 17)

The results of a 100-meter race are as follows. Instead of using names, participants were assigned numbers. Answer the following questions:

Runner	#253	#40	#685	#421	#89	#14	#26	#570
Time in seconds	13.6	15.1	14.9	14.8	13.8	14.4	15	10.4

1. In what order did the runners cross the finish line?

2. Most of the runners were fourth-graders. Which runner was most likely a professional athlete?

3. Use a calculator to find the average time for the race. (Find the mean.) Is your answer reasonable?

4. How much time passed between the times the first- and second-place winners crossed the finish line?

AT A GLANCE

Math Facts and Daily Practice and Problems

DPP Bit E requires students to choose an appropriate tool or method for computation. Task F develops number sense with money. Bit G provides practice with division facts using fact families. Challenge H provides practice in data analysis.

Part 1. Collecting the Data

1. Students answer *Questions 1–2* to identify variables on the *Rolling a Number Cube* Lab Pages in the *Student Guide.*
2. Pairs of students roll a number cube 60 times and record the results on a data table *(Question 3).*
3. Each student makes a graph of the results *(Question 4).*
4. Students pool the results of their rolls on a class data table *(Question 5).* We recommend pooling data from 10 groups, providing data from 600 rolls.
5. Students graph the class results *(Question 6).*
6. Students answer *Questions 7–8.*

Part 2. The Lab and the Game

Students refer back to the *Bean Counter's Game* and talk again about strategies *(Question 9).*

Part 3. Number Cubes and Probability

1. Students read the Number Cubes and Probability section in the *Student Guide.*
2. Students compare the results of their experiment with the probabilities by completing *Questions 10–11* on the *Rolling a Number Cube* Lab Pages in the *Student Guide.*
3. Students discuss the probabilities of various rolls by completing *Questions 12–16.*

Homework

1. *Questions 12–16* in the *Student Guide* can be used as homework.
2. Assign Home Practice Part 3 from the *Discovery Assignment Book.*
3. Students practice division facts using the *Triangle Flash Cards.*

Assessment

1. Students complete the *Check-up* Assessment Page which follows the lesson guide in the *Unit Resource Guide.*
2. Use the *Observational Assessment Record* to note students' abilities to express probabilities as fractions and to make and interpret bar graphs.

Notes:

Number Cube Rolls: Class Data Table

F Face	T Number of Times Face Appeared by Group										
	Gr. 1	Gr. 2	Gr. 3	Gr. 4	Gr. 5	Gr. 6	Gr. 7	Gr. 8	Gr. 9	Gr. 10	Total
⚀											
⚁											
⚂											
⚃											
⚄											
⚅											

Grand Total _____

Check-up

1. **A.** What is the probability of rolling a 2 when a fair number cube is rolled?

   B. What is the probability of rolling a number less than 4 when a fair number cube is rolled? Explain your thinking.

2. Sketch a graph that shows how the results might look if you rolled a fair number cube 6000 times.

Student Guide

Questions 1–16 (SG pp. 388–391)

1. *F, the faces on the cube

2. *T, the number of times each face comes up

3. *See Figure 12 in Lesson Guide 3 for a sample data table.

4. A. *See Figure 13 in Lesson Guide 3 for sample graph.

    B. *Descriptions will vary. Referring to the graph in Figure 13, students may say that the bars are of different heights, although no face appeared less than 6 times and no face appeared more than 13 times.

5. *See Figure 14 in Lesson Guide 3 for a sample class data table.

6. A. *See Figure 15 in Lesson Guide 3 for a sample graph.

    B. *Descriptions will vary. Referring to the graph in Figure 15, students may say that the bars are about the same height. The shape of the graph is almost flat.

    C. *Answers will vary. Students should note that the shape of the class graph is flatter than the 60-roll graph. The heights of the bars even out when there are more rolls.

7. Answers to *Question 7* are based on the sample data table and graph in Figures 14 and 15 in Lesson Guide 3.

    A. *600, About 100 times

    B. *Yes. The number of times each face appeared is about 100 times. Since the bars on the graph are about the same height, the data suggests the number cubes are fair.

8. No, we should suspect that the cube is not fair. With a fair cube, the probability of a 6 appearing is $\frac{1}{6}$, about 167 times in 1000 rolls. The 6 appeared on $\frac{1}{2}$ of the rolls. Even though some variation due to chance could be expected, 500 out of 1000 times is too excessive to assume the cube is fair.

9. *Distribute the beans evenly among the six possible faces.

    Answers to *Questions 10 and 11* are based on the sample data table and graph in Figures 12 through 15 in Lesson Guide 3.

10. A. No. The four only appeared 6 out of 60 times or $\frac{1}{10}$ of the time.

    B. Yes. Each face appeared about 100 times out of 600 or $\frac{1}{6}$ of the time.

11. Yes. The 5 appeared 102 times and the 6 appeared 101 times for a total of 203 times. This is very close to $\frac{1}{3}$ of 600 or 200 times.

12. A. $\frac{1}{6}$

    B. nearer "0"

13. A. 1, 3, 5

    B. $\frac{3}{6} = \frac{1}{2}$. There are 3 odd numbers so there are three chances out of six to get an odd number.

14. A. $\frac{2}{6} = \frac{1}{3}$

    B. closer to 50%

15. A. *b

    B. *The probability of rolling a 3 on any one roll is always $\frac{1}{6}$ regardless of what has been rolled before.

16. About 200, because $200 = \frac{1}{6}$ of 1200.

Discovery Assignment Book

**Home Practice (DAB p. 228)

Part 3. Multiplication and Division Practice

Questions A–N

A. 4725

B. 2114

C. 9801

D. 19,644

E. 9394

F. 347

G. 4638

H. 92 R2

I. 1664 R3

J. 419 R1

K. 558

L. 1100

M. Possible strategy for H: $720 \div 8 = 90$.

N. Possible strategy for B: $302 \times 7 = 300 \times 7 + 300 \times 2 = 2114$.

*Answers and/or discussion are included in the Lesson Guide.

**Answers for all the Home Practice in the *Discovery Assignment Book* are at the end of the unit.

Unit Resource Guide

Check-up (URG p. 44)

Questions 1–2

1. **A.** $\frac{1}{6}$

    B. There are three numbers less than 4 (3, 2, and 1) on a number cube, so there are 3 out of 6 chances of rolling one of those numbers. Therefore, the probability of rolling a number less than 4 is $\frac{3}{6} = \frac{1}{2}$.

2.

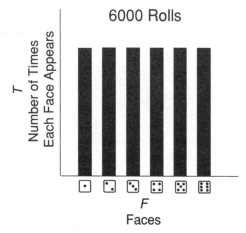

*Answers and/or discussion are included in the Lesson Guide.

**Answers for all the Home Practice in the *Discovery Assignment Book* are at the end of the unit.

LESSON GUIDE

From Number Cubes to Spinners

Estimated Class Sessions: 1

Students use their growing understanding of chance to build spinners which reflect the same probabilities as a number cube.

Key Content

- Collecting, organizing, graphing, and analyzing data.

- Making and interpreting bar graphs.

- Dividing a circle by drawing angles using a protractor.

- Exploring situations that have outcomes that are equally likely.

- Collecting and analyzing data from a random process.

- Comparing probabilities with real-world data: spinning a spinner.

- Identifying patterns that emerge as the number of random events increases.

Daily Practice and Problems: Bit for Lesson 4

I. Lines (URG p. 17)

1. List all pairs of lines that appear to be parallel in the drawing.

2. List the pairs of lines that appear to be perpendicular to each other.

DPP Task is on page 51. Suggestions for using the DPPs are on page 51.

Curriculum Sequence

Before This Unit

Making Spinners. Students designed spinners using protractors in Unit 9 Lesson 3 *Shapes and Solids.*

Materials List

Print Materials for Students

	Math Facts and Daily Practice and Problems	Activity	Homework
Student Books			
Student Guide		*From Number Cubes to Spinners* Page 392	
Discovery Assignment Book		*A Spinner for a Number Cube* Page 231	Home Practice Part 2 Page 227
Teacher Resources			
Unit Resource Guide	DPP Items I–J Pages 17–18 ⊚		
Generic Section ⊚		Centimeter Graph Paper, 1 per student and Three-column Data Table, 1 per student	

⊚ available on Teacher Resource CD

All Transparency Masters, Blackline Masters, and Assessment Blackline Masters in the Unit Resource Guide are on the Teacher Resource CD.

Supplies for Each Student Pair

protractor
clear plastic spinner or paper clip

Materials for the Teacher

From Number Cubes to Spinners: Class Data Table Transparency Master (Unit Resource Guide) Page 53
Number Cube Rolls: Class Data Table Transparency Master prepared in Lesson 3
large poster paper or transparency of a class data table for Lesson 3, optional
protractor

Developing the Activity

Students begin the activity by reading the opening paragraph on the *From Number Cubes to Spinners* Activity Page in the *Student Guide.* Two students cannot play a game because they have lost a number cube. They decide to make a spinner that will give the same results as a number cube.

Discuss **Questions 1–4** with the class. Students must consider the characteristics of a spinner that will give the same results as a number cube. Since a number cube has six faces that are equally likely, the spinner should have six regions that are equally likely. To divide the circle into six regions of equal area, each angle on the spinner should measure 360° ÷ 6 or 60°. See Figure 16.

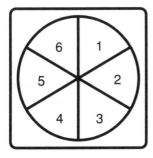

Figure 16: *A spinner that reflects the same probabilities as a number cube*

At this point in the lesson, students use protractors to make spinners on the *A Spinner for a Number Cube* Activity Page in the *Discovery Assignment Book.* Have students show their spinners to the class and explain their thinking about the divisions of the circle.

Question 6 in the *Student Guide* asks students to check their spinners by spinning and recording 60 spins. Although this number is not large enough to guarantee a trend toward an equal distribution (assuming the spinner was correctly constructed), a pattern should begin to emerge. Students should record their data as they did for the number cubes in Lesson 3. See Figures 11 and 12 in Lesson 3. This may be done at home for homework.

From Number Cubes to Spinners

Tanya and Grace want to play a game after school at Tanya's house. They read in the directions that they need a number cube to play the game, but they can't find one anywhere. Finally Tanya had an idea, "Maybe we can make a spinner that will work the same way a number cube does when we play the game. All we need is a paper clip, a pencil, some paper, and a protractor."

1. What is the probability of rolling each face on a fair number cube?
2. What would a spinner look like that would give the same results as a number cube?
3. How many regions would be on such a spinner?
4. What would be the measure of each angle on the spinner?

5. Create a spinner which will give the same results as a number cube. Use the *A Spinner for a Number Cube* Activity Page in the *Discovery Assignment Book* and a protractor to help you.
6. Test your spinner. Spin your spinner 60 times and record the number of times the spinner lands in each region.
7. Share your data with the class. Record your data on a class data table.
8. A. Make a bar graph of the class data.
   B. Describe the graph.
9. Compare the graph of the class data for the spinners to the graph of the class data for the number cubes in the lab in Lesson 3.
   A. How many bars does each graph have?
   B. Are the shapes of the graphs similar to one another?
10. Will your spinner give the same results as a number cube? Why or why not?

392 SG · Grade 4 · Unit 14 · Lesson 4   From Number Cubes to Spinners

Student Guide - Page 392

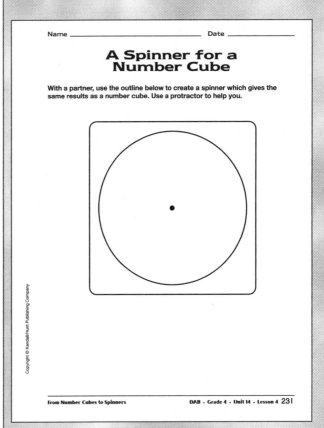

Name _____ Date _____

A Spinner for a Number Cube

With a partner, use the outline below to create a spinner which gives the same results as a number cube. Use a protractor to help you.

From Number Cubes to Spinners   DAB · Grade 4 · Unit 14 · Lesson 4   231

Discovery Assignment Book - Page 231

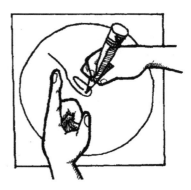

Figure 17: *Using a pencil and a paper clip as a spinner*

Collect class data from spinners divided into 6 equal regions as in Lesson 3 *(Question 7)*. You may use the *From Number Cubes to Spinners: Class Data Table* Transparency Master or students can record the data in a class data table written on the board or large poster paper. The number of times the spinner lands in each region should be about the same if many spins are taken.

To complete *Question 8,* students make a bar graph of the class data on *Centimeter Graph Paper* and describe the graph. *Question 9* asks students to compare the class graph for the spinners to the class graph for the number cubes from Lesson 3. Discuss the similarities. If many trials are included in the data for each graph, both the graphs should have the same general shape. Since the probability of each of the six faces appearing is equally likely and the probability of the spinner landing in each region is equally likely, both graphs should have six bars of (about) equal height. *Question 10* asks students if they think their spinners will give the same results as a number cube. Since the probabilities for the spinner and the number cube are the same, they should both give the same results.

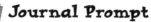

Journal Prompt

How would a spinner look that reflects a greater chance of spinning a 4 than the other numbers? Sketch a spinner to help explain.

Suggestions for Teaching the Lesson

Homework and Practice

- Students can test their spinners at home for homework (**Question 6** in the *Student Guide*) and then report their findings the next day in class.

- DPP Bit I is a review of geometric parallel and perpendicular lines. Task J provides practice with addition and subtraction of large numbers using mental math.

- Home Practice Part 2 in the *Discovery Assignment Book* is a set of word problems.

Answers for Part 2 of the Home Practice can be found in the Answer Key at the end of this lesson and at the end of this unit.

Assessment

The Journal Prompt can help assess students' understanding of probability concepts.

Extension

Ask students to make and test a spinner that has 4 regions (A, B, C, D) with the following probabilities:

Probability of A $= \frac{1}{2}$

Probability of B $= \frac{1}{4}$

Probability of C $= \frac{1}{8}$

Probability of D $= \frac{1}{8}$

Daily Practice and Problems: Task for Lesson 4

J. Task: Adding and Subtracting
(URG p. 18)

Solve the following problems in your head.

1. A. $1700 + 400 =$

   B. $4300 - 400 =$

   C. $1450 + 350 =$

   D. $1658 - 500 =$

   E. $5033 + 9100 =$

   F. $2099 + 301 =$

2. Explain your strategy for Questions 1C and 1D.

Discovery Assignment Book - Page 227

AT A GLANCE

Math Facts and Daily Practice and Problems

DPP Bit I is a review of geometry. Task J provides practice in mental math.

Developing the Activity

1. Use the opening paragraph and *Questions 1–4* on the *From Number Cubes to Spinners* Activity Page in the *Student Guide* to discuss how a spinner must look to give the same results as a number cube.
2. Remind students of the technique they learned in Unit 9 of using a protractor to draw angles so they can divide a circle into regions of equal area.
3. Student pairs make spinners divided into six equal regions *(Question 5)*.
4. Students check their spinners by spinning 60 times and recording their results *(Question 6)*.
5. Compile class data from spinners *(Question 7)*.
6. Graph the class data and compare the shape of this graph to the shape of the graph in Lesson 3 *(Questions 8–10)*.

Homework

1. Students can test their spinners at home for homework *(Question 6)*.
2. Assign Home Practice Part 2 in the *Discovery Assignment Book*.

Assessment

Use the Journal Prompt to assess students' understanding of this concept.

Notes:

From Number Cubes to Spinners:
Class Data Table

R Region	Number of Times Spinner Lands in Region by Group										
	Gr. 1	Gr. 2	Gr. 3	Gr. 4	Gr. 5	Gr. 6	Gr. 7	Gr. 8	Gr. 9	Gr. 10	Total
1											
2											
3											
4											
5											
6											

Grand Total ____

Student Guide

Questions 1–10 (SG p. 392)

1. *$\frac{1}{6}$

2. *The spinner should have six regions of equal area, each angle measuring 60°.

3. *6 regions

4. *60°

5.

6. *Answers will vary.

7. *Answers will vary.

8. **A.** Answers will vary.

   B. Each bar will be about the same height. The shape of the graph can be described as almost flat.

9. *The graph of a large number of spins (600 spins) of a spinner with 6 equal regions should look very similar to a graph of 600 rolls of a fair number cube as shown in Figure 15 of the Lesson Guide 3.

   A. *6 bars

   B. *The shapes of both graphs are very similar. They can be described as flat.

10. *Yes. The data collected for a spinner with 6 equal regions is very similar to the data collected for a fair number cube.

Discovery Assignment Book

**Home Practice (DAB p. 227)

Part 2. School Supplies

Questions 1–4

1. Jessie's supplies—$7.84
   Jacob's supplies—$7.18

2. Jessie's

3. $0.66

4. Answers will vary.

*Answers and/or discussion are included in the Lesson Guide.
**Answers for all the Home Practice in the *Discovery Assignment Book* are at the end of the unit.

LESSON GUIDE

Exploring Spinners

Estimated
Class
Sessions:
2

Students use various spinners to explore ideas about probability. The probability line is revisited. A quiz on the probabilities of spinners is included in this lesson.

Key Content

- Exploring situations that have outcomes that are not equally likely.
- Comparing probabilities with real-world data: spinning spinners.
- Expressing probabilities as fractions.
- Using the word "or" in a probability problem.
- Collecting, organizing, graphing, and analyzing data.
- Making and interpreting bar graphs.

Key Vocabulary

fair spinner

Daily Practice and Problems:
Bits for Lesson 5

K. Still More Division Facts (URG p. 18)

Complete the table using division. Use the number in the first column as your divisor. Write your answer (the quotient) in the empty boxes.

÷	10	20	30	40	50	100
2						
5						
10						

What patterns do you see?

M. Division Facts Quiz 1
   (URG p. 19)

A. $35 \div 7 =$ B. $64 \div 8 =$

C. $14 \div 2 =$ D. $80 \div 8 =$

E. $8 \div 4 =$ F. $16 \div 4 =$

G. $50 \div 10 =$ H. $36 \div 6 =$

I. $9 \div 3 =$ J. $100 \div 10 =$

K. $30 \div 5 =$ L. $40 \div 4 =$

M. $18 \div 9 =$ N. $6 \div 2 =$

O. $25 \div 5 =$ P. $5 \div 5 =$

DPP Tasks are on page 63. Suggestions for using the DPPs are on page 63.

Materials List

	Math Facts and Daily Practice and Problems	Activity	Written Assessment
Student Books — Student Guide		*Exploring Spinners* Pages 393–396	
Discovery Assignment Book		*Exploring Spinners* 1 and 2 Page 233	
Teacher Resources — Facts Resource Guide ⊙	DPP Items 14K & 14M		DPP Item 14M *Division Facts Quiz 1*
Unit Resource Guide	DPP Items K–N Pages 18–20 ⊙		DPP Item M *Division Facts Quiz 1* Page 19 ⊙ and *Spinners Quiz* Page 65, 1 per student
Generic Section ⊙		*Centimeter Graph Paper,* 2 per student	

⊙ available on Teacher Resource CD

All Transparency Masters, Blackline Masters, and Assessment Blackline Masters in the Unit Resource Guide are on the Teacher Resource CD.

Supplies for Each Student Pair or Group

clear plastic spinner or paper clips

Materials for the Teacher

Observational Assessment Record (Unit Resource Guide, Pages 9–10 and Teacher Resource CD)
Individual Assessment Record Sheet (Teacher Implementation Guide, Assessment section and Teacher Resource CD)
2 copies of *Spinners Class Data Table* Transparency Master (Unit Resource Guide) Page 66 or large poster paper, optional

R Region	N Number of Times Spinner Landed in Region by Group										
	Gr. 1	Gr. 2	Gr. 3	Gr. 4	Gr. 5	Gr. 6	Gr. 7	Gr. 8	Gr. 9	Gr. 10	Total
Yellow											
Red											
Blue											
Green											

Grand Total _____

Figure 18: *Spinners Class Data Table*

Before the Activity

Draw two tables on the board or large sheet of poster paper like the one in Figure 18 or use the *Spinners Class Data Table* Transparency Master.

Developing the Activity

This activity continues the exploration of spinners begun in Lesson 4 *From Number Cubes to Spinners*. Each pair of students will use two different spinners as shown on the *Exploring Spinners* Activity Pages in the *Student Guide*. Larger copies of these spinners for the students to use are located on the *Exploring Spinners 1 and 2* Activity Page in the *Discovery Assignment Book*.

The procedure, as outlined in the *Student Guide*, is the same for both spinners and is similar to work done in the previous two lessons. (See *Questions 1–5* for directions for Spinner 1 and *Questions 12–15* for Spinner 2.)

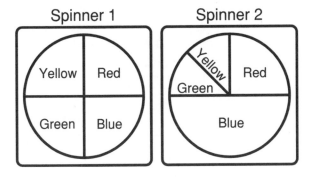

Figure 19: *Spinners 1 and 2*

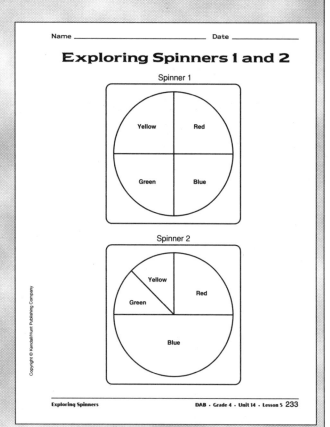

Discovery Assignment Book - Page 233

Student Guide - Page 393

Spinner 1 has four regions, each with the same area. Spinner 2 also has four regions, but the regions do not all have the same area. See Figure 19. Ask:

- *What do you notice that is different about the two spinners?* (One has equal regions or sections, the other does not.)

- *Do you think this will make a difference when we spin? Why?* (Yes. On Spinner 2, the area of blue is the largest, so there is more space for the spinner to land on blue. Red is the next largest so it also has more space for the spinner to land, but not as much space as blue. Yellow and green have the smallest amount of space for the spinner to land. There is more of a chance for the spinner to land on blue or red.)

- *Which one of these is like a fair number cube? Why?* (Spinner 1, because each of the regions has the same amount of space for the spinner to land. Each region has the same probability of occurring.)

- *Which one of these spinners is fair?* (Spinner 1)

- *What is the probability of getting blue on Spinner 1? Red? Yellow? Green?* (Each has the same probability of occurring: one chance in 4, or $\frac{1}{4}$.)

- *Are the probabilities the same for the different regions in Spinner 2? Why or why not?* (No, because the regions have different areas, the spinner will land on blue more often than it will land on yellow or green.)

Part 1. Exploring Spinner 1

In *Question 1A* students make a table and predict the number of times Spinner 1 will land in each region if they spin it 40 times. They should be able to predict that the spinner will land 10 times in each region. Students then spin the spinner 40 times and record their results, using their own paper *(Question 1B)*. As students are spinning their spinners, circulate about the room to see if there are students who were not able to predict appropriately. *Question 2* asks them to compare their results to their predictions. Since the sample is small, the results will probably not match the predictions exactly. The results may not even be very close.

In order for students to work with a larger sample, the class pools their data. *Question 3* asks students to first sketch (or describe in words) what they think a graph of all the data in the class will look like. Students do not need to predict the exact height of each bar. Encourage them to predict the size of the bars in relation to one another. For example, if students understand the probabilities represented by Spinner 1, they can predict that the bars on the graph will all be about the same height. They might describe the shape of the graph as flat.

When students have recorded their predictions in words or drawings, they pool their data to obtain results for the entire class *(Question 4)*. See the sample data table and graph in Figures 20 and 21. They can record the class data on the *Spinners Class Data Table* Transparency Master. Students transfer the class data to the last column of their individual data tables and make bar graphs of the class data *(Question 5)*. Remind students that the total number of spins in the third column of their own data tables should be 40 and the total number of spins in the last column of the class data table should equal the total number of spins made by the class.

Spinner 1 Data

Region	Predicted Number of Times Spinner Will Land in Region (Out of 40)	Number of Times Spinner Landed in Region (Out of 40)	Class Data: Total Number of Times Spinner Landed in Region (Out of _400_)
Yellow	10	‖‖ ‖‖ ‖ = 12	116
Red	10	‖‖ ‖‖‖ = 9	90
Blue	10	‖‖ ‖‖ ‖ = 11	96
Green	10	‖‖ ‖‖ = 8	98

Figure 20: *Sample data table for Spinner 1*

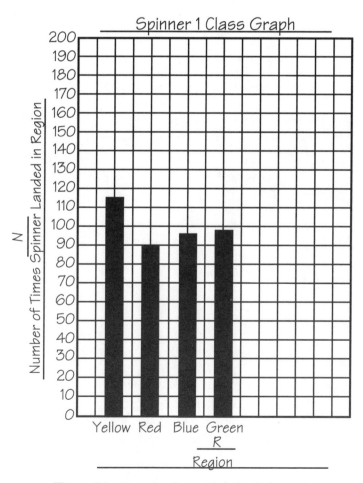

Figure 21: *Sample class graph for Spinner 1*

TIMS Tip

Students will be more able to compare the class graphs for the two spinners if the same scale is used for both spinners. For our sample, the vertical axis is scaled by tens on both graphs.

6. Is the shape of your predicted graph for the class data similar to the shape of the class graph?

7. Draw a probability line on your paper. Each of the following statements has a letter in front of it. Use the letter to place the statement correctly on the line.
   A. The probability of the spinner landing on yellow.
   B. The probability of the spinner landing on green.
   C. The probability of the spinner landing in a purple region.
   D. The probability of the spinner landing in a region other than yellow.

8. Choose the probability that will correctly complete this statement: The chance of spinning yellow is (a) one in four, (b) one in six, or (c) three in four.

9. Write the probability of spinning yellow as a fraction.

10. What is the probability of the spinner landing on yellow or green? The word "or" has a special meaning in math. This question asks for the probability of the spinner landing in the area covered by stripes in the picture.

Spinner 1

11. Write the probability of the spinner landing on red, blue, or green.

Exploring Spinner 2

You and a partner are going to spin 40 times using Spinner 2. You will need a copy of Spinner 2 and a piece of *Centimeter Graph Paper* to complete this part of the lesson.

12. Draw a data table for Spinner 2 just like the table for Spinner 1.

Spinner 2

   A. Before you begin to collect data for Spinner 2, predict the number of times the spinner will land in each region. Record your predictions in your data table.
   B. Spin 40 times and record your results.

Exploring Spinners

Student Guide - Page 394

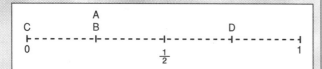

Figure 22: *A completed probability line for* **Question 7**

Question 6 asks if the shapes of their predicted graphs for Spinner 1 are similar to the graphs of the actual data. Ask:

- *Are most of the bars about the same height?* (Yes, but not exactly.)
- *Why do you think the bars are not the exact same height?* (Answers may vary. When a random event occurs a relatively small number of times, the numbers usually do not match the mathematical probability exactly.)
- *Were your numbers for the different regions exactly alike when your group did the 40 spins?* (No.)
- *Are the bars of the class graph closer to each other than the numbers you got in your own group?* (Yes, they should be.)
- *What do you think the bars of the graph would look like if we used 40 spins from 100 students for 4000 spins? 200 students for 8000 spins?* (The bars will get more and more even.)

Question 7 asks students to show probabilities involving Spinner 1 on a probability line. (Probability lines were introduced in Lesson 1.) For example, ***Question 7A*** asks students to place the probability of landing in the yellow region on the line. Since the probability of landing in the yellow region is $\frac{1}{4}$, they should place an A one-fourth of the way between 0 and 1. Figure 22 shows a completed line.

Students find probabilities for spins on Spinner 1 in ***Questions 8–9. Questions 10–11*** discuss the use of the word "or" in a mathematical statement. Ask:

- *Imagine you are playing a game and the rule is that you get a point for the spinner landing on "yellow or green." What is the probability that you will land on yellow?* ($\frac{1}{4}$)
- *Do you get a point for yellow?* (Yes)
- *What is the probability that you will land on green?* ($\frac{1}{4}$)
- *Do you get a point for green?* (Yes)
- *What is the probability for getting a point when you spin the spinner?* (You get a point for landing on either yellow or green, so $\frac{1}{4} + \frac{1}{4} = \frac{2}{4}$ or $\frac{1}{2}$.)

Part 2. Exploring Spinner 2

The class repeats the same procedure for Spinner 2. The students have already determined that Spinner 2 is not a fair spinner. Ask:

- *Will the spinner land in the different regions an equal number of times?* (No)
- *Which region will get hit the most?* (Blue) *the least?* (Yellow or green)

- *How much bigger is the blue region than the red?* (2 times as big) *How much bigger is the red region than the yellow or green?* (2 times as big) *How much bigger is the blue region than the yellow or green?* (4 times as big)
- *What will this do to the number of times the spinner will land in each region?* (The blue will get 2 times as many hits as red and 4 times as many hits as yellow and green. Yellow and green should be about the same.)
- *What will it do to the bars in the bar graph?* (The blue will be about 2 times as tall as red; red will be about 2 times as tall as the yellow and green bars.)

Students write their predictions for 40 spins of Spinner 2 and spin their spinners *(Question 12)*. In *Questions 13–15,* they write or draw a prediction for the shape of the class bar graph, pool their results on *Spinners Class Data Table,* and draw a bar graph of the class data.

When students compare their predicted graphs to their graphs of the actual data *(Question 16),* they should again look at the general shape of the two graphs and not expect the actual data to match the predictions exactly. A sample data table and class graph for Spinner 2 is shown in Figures 23 and 24.

Spinner 2 Data

Region	Predicted Number of Times Spinner Will Land in Region (Out of 40)	Number of Times Spinner Landed in Region (Out of 40)	Class Data: Total Number of Times Spinner Landed in Region (Out of __400__)
Yellow	5	⊬⊬⊬ = 5	45
Red	10	⊬⊬⊬ //// = 9	100
Blue	20	⊬⊬⊬ ⊬⊬⊬ ⊬⊬⊬ /// = 18	190
Green	5	⊬⊬⊬ /// = 8	65

Figure 23: *Sample data table for Spinner 2*

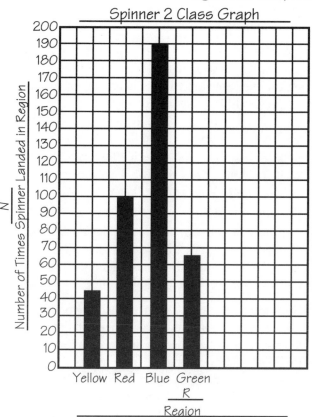

Figure 24: *Sample class graph for Spinner 2*

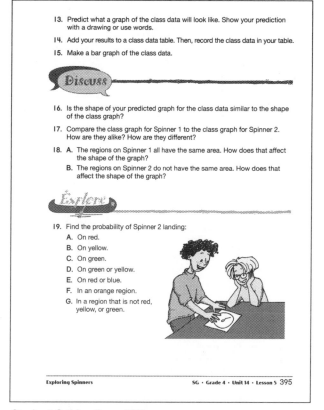

13. Predict what a graph of the class data will look like. Show your prediction with a drawing or use words.

14. Add your results to a class data table. Then, record the class data in your table.

15. Make a bar graph of the class data.

Discuss

16. Is the shape of your predicted graph for the class data similar to the shape of the class graph?

17. Compare the class graph for Spinner 1 to the class graph for Spinner 2. How are they alike? How are they different?

18. A. The regions on Spinner 1 all have the same area. How does that affect the shape of the graph?

    B. The regions on Spinner 2 do not have the same area. How does that affect the shape of the graph?

Explore

19. Find the probability of Spinner 2 landing:
    A. On red.
    B. On yellow.
    C. On green.
    D. On green or yellow.
    E. On red or blue.
    F. In an orange region.
    G. In a region that is not red, yellow, or green.

Student Guide - Page 395

Questions 17–18 ask students to compare the two spinners and the resulting data and class graphs. Encourage students to connect the shapes of the graphs to the regions on the spinners. If the regions on a spinner have equal area as on Spinner 1, the probabilities of the spinner landing in each area are equally likely. This spinner will produce data that is represented by a graph with bars of about equal height. If the regions on a spinner do not have equal area, the probabilities associated with the regions on the spinner will not be equal. The heights of the bars on the corresponding graph will not be equal and will reflect the size of each region. *Question 19* is appropriate to assign as homework.

Part 3. Probability Problems

Questions 20–24 review the concepts covered in this unit. The questions may be assigned for homework or completed in class.

Questions 20–24 expand upon the students' experience with spinners and number cubes. Students predict outcomes and calculate probabilities, writing the probabilities as fractions. In *Question 21A,* students calculate the probabilities for a number cube whose six faces show only two colors. *Question 21B* reviews whether the probability for an event changes because of the outcomes of preceding events. Even though the cube has landed on red for five consecutive rolls, the probability for red on the next roll remains $\frac{1}{2}$. *Question 22* discusses the probability involved in tossing a coin.

Question 23 introduces a new context for calculating probability, drawing names from a hat. Since there are four possible outcomes and each is equally likely, the probability of drawing Tess's name is one in four, or $\frac{1}{4}$. Discuss with the students the elements of fairness in this context. Remind them of their discussions of fairness working with number cubes and spinners. Ask:

- *Would it be possible for Abby's drawing to not be a fair one?* (Yes)

- *How can Abby make sure that her drawing is fair?* (Write all the names on same color and same size paper, all names folded the same way, close her eyes when drawing, etc.)

Question 24 presents a novel probability problem using spinners in a game. The regions on the spinner are not equal but neither are the points allowed. Region A has twice as much area, but receives half the number of points as the other two areas. Have students work at this problem, either individually or with a partner, before discussing with the class. The end

---

Probability Problems

20. **A.** When you spin this spinner, what is the probability that this spinner will land on A?

 B. Danny spins the spinner 150 times. About how many times do you expect it to land on A?

21. Tim painted 3 sides of a cube red and 3 sides blue.
 A. What is the probability that a red side will come up when the cube is rolled?
 B. Tim rolls the cube 5 times and it comes up red each time. What is the probability that it will come up red on the next roll?

22. **A.** What two ways can a nickel land when it is tossed into the air?
 B. What is the probability that a nickel will land "heads up" when it is tossed in the air?
 C. Jenny tosses a nickel 100 times. About how many times do you expect it to land heads up?

23. Abby wanted to invite a friend over to play, but she couldn't decide who to call. She put the names of Erin, Whitney, Tess, and Sam into a hat, closed her eyes, and pulled out a name. What is the probability that she chose Tess?

24. Peter, Nick, and Nate play a spinner game. Before playing, they agree that Peter will have Region A, Nick will have Region B, and Nate will have Region C. If the spinner lands in a player's region, he scores the point or points for that region. Do you think this is a fair game? That is, do you think each boy has an equal chance of winning? Explain your thinking.

396 SG · Grade 4 · Unit 14 · Lesson 5   **Exploring Spinners**

Student Guide - Page 396

result of the game is that it is fair. The differences between areas and points balance each other out. Have students discuss and explain their thinking.

Suggestions for Teaching the Lesson

Math Facts

DPP Bit K provides practice with division facts.

Homework and Practice

- Assign *Question 19* on the *Exploring Spinners* Activity Pages in the *Student Guide* as homework.
- DPP Task L provides practice in computation. Task N provides practice expressing probabilities as fractions.

Assessment

- Use the *Observational Assessment Record* to note students' abilities to use probabilities to make predictions.
- Use *Questions 18–19* to assess students' abilities to recognize and quantify different probabilities in spinning spinners.
- Use the *Spinners Quiz* Assessment Blackline Master to evaluate students' understanding of the probability concepts involved in spinning spinners. If you plan to complete Lesson 6 *Make Your Own Spinners,* delay the quiz until after that lesson.
- DPP Bit M is a quiz on half the division facts for the 2s, 5s, 10s, and square numbers. The other half of the division facts are on the quiz in Bit O in Lesson 7.
- Transfer appropriate documentation from the Unit 14 *Observational Assessment Record* to the students' *Individual Assessment Record Sheets.*

Daily Practice and Problems: Tasks for Lesson 5

L. Task: Multiplication and Division Practice (URG p. 19)

Solve the following using paper-and-pencil methods or mental math. Estimate to make sure your answers are reasonable.

1. A. $23 \times 64 =$ B. $48 \times 93 =$

    C. $91 \times 46 =$ D. $57 \times 70 =$

    E. $173 \div 5 =$ F. $2106 \div 6 =$

    G. $3590 \div 7 =$ H. $7853 \div 9 =$

2. Explain your estimation strategy for Question 1B.

N. Task: Probability: Number Cubes (URG p. 20)

Irma found a strange number cube. It had six faces but did not have the numbers 1 through 6 on it. It had the following numbers: 4, 4, 4, 5, 5, and 6.

1. What is the probability that Irma will roll a 6?

2. What is the probability that Irma will roll a 4?

3. What is the probability that Irma will roll a 5?

4. What is the probability that Irma will roll an even number?

AT A GLANCE

Math Facts and Daily Practice and Problems

DPP Bit K provides division facts practice. Bit M is a division facts quiz. Task L is multiplication and division computation. Task N reviews probability concepts.

Part 1. Exploring Spinner 1

1. The class makes predictions about Spinner 1, shown on the *Exploring Spinners* Activity Pages in the *Student Guide (Questions 1A)*.
2. Each student pair or group spins 40 times using Spinner 1 on the *Exploring Spinners 1 and 2* Activity Page in the *Discovery Assignment Book (Question 1B)*.
3. Student pairs compare their results with their predictions and compile a class set of data *(Questions 2–3)*.
4. Each student graphs the class data *(Question 5)*.
5. Each student answers a set of questions about the spinner in the *Student Guide (Questions 6–11)*.

Part 2. Exploring Spinner 2

1. Repeat the process with the second spinner *(Questions 12–16)*.
2. Students compare the class graphs for the two spinners *(Questions 17–18)*.

Part 3. Probability Problems

Students complete *Questions 20–24* in small groups in class or for homework.

Homework

Assign *Questions 19A–G* in the *Student Guide.*

Assessment

1. Use the *Observational Assessment Record* to note students' abilities to use probabilities to make predictions.
2. Use the *Spinners Quiz* to evaluate students' understanding of probability.
3. DPP Bit M is a quiz on the division facts for the 2s, 5s, 10s, and the square numbers.
4. Transfer appropriate documentation from the Unit 14 *Observational Assessment Record* to the students' *Individual Assessment Record Sheets*.

Notes:

Spinners Quiz

Professor Peabody designed this spinner for a game.

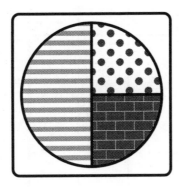

I. Draw a probability line. Each of the following statements about Professor Peabody's spinner has a letter in front of it. Use the letter to place the probability correctly on the line.

   A. The probability of the spinner landing on dots.

   B. The probability of the spinner landing on stripes.

   C. The probability of the spinner landing on stripes or dots.

   D. The probability of the spinner landing in a blank region.

2. **A.** What is the probability of the spinner landing on bricks? Write the probability as a fraction.

   B. What is the probability of the spinner landing on bricks or dots? Write the probability as a fraction.

3. **A.** If you collect data for 800 spins, about how many times do you expect the spinner to land on stripes?

   B. About how many times do you expect the spinner to land on dots?

Spinners Class Data Table

R Region	N Number of Times Spinner Landed in Region by Group										
	Gr. 1	Gr. 2	Gr. 3	Gr. 4	Gr. 5	Gr. 6	Gr. 7	Gr. 8	Gr. 9	Gr. 10	Total
Yellow											
Red											
Blue											
Green											

Grand Total _____

Transparency Master

Student Guide

Questions 1–24 (SG pp. 393–396)

1. **A.** *See Figure 20 in Lesson Guide 5 for a sample data table with sample predictions.

   B. *See Figure 20 in Lesson Guide 5 for sample data.

2. *Answers will vary.

3. *

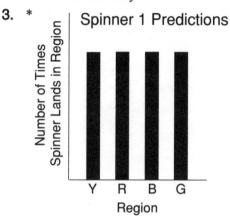

Spinner 1 Predictions

4. *See Figure 20 in Lesson Guide 5 for sample data.

5. *See Figure 21 in Lesson Guide 5 for a sample graph.

6. *Answers will vary.

7. *See the probability line in Figure 22 in Lesson Guide 5.

8. a; one in four

9. $\frac{1}{4}$ 10. *$\frac{1}{2}$ 11. $\frac{3}{4}$

12. *See Figure 23 in Lesson Guide 5 for a sample data table.

13. *

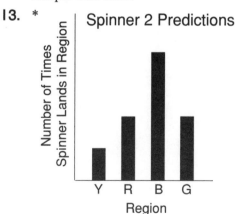

Spinner 2 Predictions

14. *See Figure 23 in Lesson Guide 5 for a sample data table.

15. *See Figure 24 in Lesson Guide 5 for a sample class graph.

16. *Answers will vary.

17. *Answers will vary. The shape of the graph for Spinner 1 in Figure 20 is much flatter than the shape of the graph of Spinner 2. Both graphs have the same number of bars.

18. **A.** *The bars are almost the same height.

    B. *The bars are different heights. The larger the region, the taller the bar.

19. **A.** $\frac{1}{4}$ **B.** $\frac{1}{8}$ **C.** $\frac{1}{8}$ **D.** $\frac{1}{4}$
    E. $\frac{3}{4}$ **F.** 0   **G.** $\frac{1}{2}$

20. **A.** $\frac{1}{3}$

    B. About 50 times

21. **A.** *$\frac{3}{6}$ or $\frac{1}{2}$

    B. $\frac{1}{2}$; because the probability does not depend on previous rolls.

22. **A.** heads up or tails up   **B.** $\frac{1}{2}$

    C. About 50 times

23. *$\frac{1}{4}$

24. *Yes. Even though the probability of landing in each region is not equal, the distribution of the points makes it a fair game. For example, the spinner should land in Region A about twice as often as it lands in Region B. However, Nate will score 2 points each time it lands in Region B and Peter will only score 1 point when it lands in Region A.

Unit Resource Guide

Spinners Quiz (URG p. 65)

Questions 1–3

1.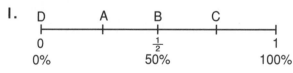

2. **A.** $\frac{1}{4}$ **B.** $\frac{1}{2}$

3. **A.** 400 times   **B.** 200 times

*Answers and/or discussion are included in the Lesson Guide.
**Answers for all the Home Practice in the *Discovery Assignment Book* are at the end of the unit.

OPTIONAL LESSON

LESSON GUIDE 6

Make Your Own Spinners

Estimated Class Sessions: 1

Students work in groups to design spinners that reflect specific probabilities. If students are to complete this lesson, they should delay taking the *Spinners Quiz* found in Lesson Guide 5 until the end of this lesson.

Key Content

* Creating spinners from spin data.
* Interpreting bar graphs.
* Using probabilities to make predictions.
* Comparing probabilities to real-world data.

Materials List

Print Materials for Students

		Optional Activity
Student Books	Student Guide	*Make Your Own Spinners* Pages 397–399
	Discovery Assignment Book	*Blank Spinners* Pages 235–236

◉ *available on Teacher Resource CD*

All Transparency Masters, Blackline Masters, and Assessment Blackline Masters in the Unit Resource Guide are on the Teacher Resource CD.

Supplies for Each Student Pair

clear plastic spinner or paper clip
ruler

Developing the Activity

To begin the activity, students read through *Question 1* on the *Make Your Own Spinners* Activity Pages in the *Student Guide.* Professor Peabody is designing games which use spinners. Students are asked to design a spinner that will produce data similar to that represented in a graph. Explain to students that this activity is the reverse of that in Lessons 4 and 5. In those lessons, they were given the spinners from which they predicted the results. In this activity, they are given the results and are asked to decide what kind of spinner produced those results.

The graph of the data for Game 1 shows that Professor Peabody wanted a spinner that would land in each region 200 out of 600 times. Students will probably suggest that this was produced by a spinner with three regions of equal area. If they were to test their prediction by spinning their spinners 600 times, they probably would not come up with exactly the same data because of chance variations. However, we would expect the results to be close. Students use rulers and the *Blank Spinners* Activity Pages in the *Discovery Assignment Book* to make their spinners. They can use the tick marks on the spinners to help them divide the circle into three equal parts.

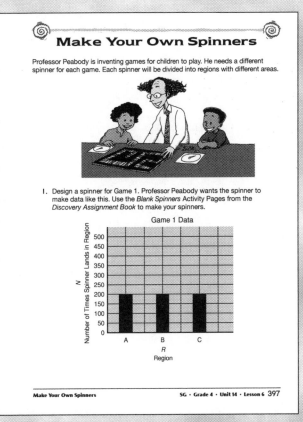

Student Guide - Page 397

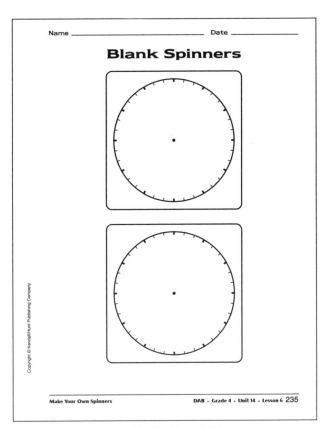

Discovery Assignment Book - Page 235

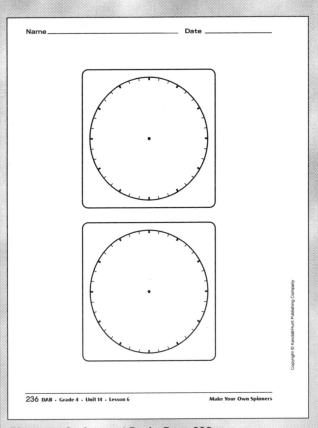

Discovery Assignment Book - Page 236

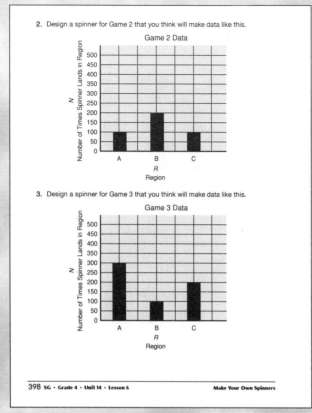

If students have trouble getting started, use the prompts below as necessary to help them begin. The graph for **Question 2** is used as an example. Figure 25 shows the graph for **Question 2** with the correct spinner.

- *Is each spin equally likely? Are all the bars the same height?* (No, no)

- *How many regions will you make? How many bars are on the graph?* (3, 3)

- *Are any of the bars the same height? If so, which ones? What does that tell you about the regions for these bars?* (Regions with the same area will produce bars which have approximately the same height. The bars for Regions A and C are the same height, so the area of Regions A and C should have the same area.)

- *How many times taller is the bar for Region B than for Region A? How many times larger will you make the area of Region B than the area of Region A?* (The bar for Region B is twice as tall as the bar for Region A, so the area of Region B should be twice as large as the area for Region A.)

- *How many total spins does the graph represent?* (400)

- *How many spins does the bar for Region B represent?* (200)

- *What fraction of the total spins does the bar for Region B represent?* (200 out of 400 or $\frac{1}{2}$)

- *What part of the circle should you make Region B?* ($\frac{1}{2}$)

- *What part of the circle should you make Region A?* ($\frac{1}{4}$)

- *What part of the circle should you make Region C?* ($\frac{1}{4}$)

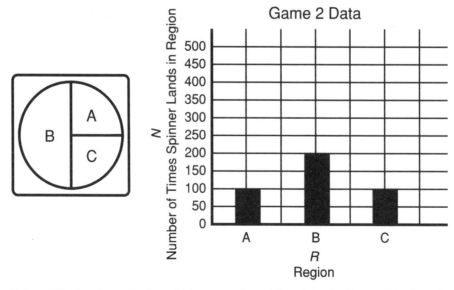

Figure 25: *A spinner that could have produced the data for Game 2 in* **Question 2**

Once students understand the process of making spinners to match graphs, they can make the spinners for **Questions 2–4.** Each group can design each spinner. Or, the class can be divided into three groups and each group can design a spinner for one of the three remaining data tables. The groups can then share their results with the rest of the class.

In **Question 5** students choose a spinner they have designed and test it. If all the groups created all the spinners, ask the class as a whole to choose one spinner to test and pool their data for the spinner. If each group developed just one spinner, then have each group test its own spinners. To test the spinners, students must spin enough times to see definite trends. They do not need to spin the same number of spins as represented on the graph, however. For example, the Game 2 Data represents 400 spins. The class can either spin a total of 400 times to check the data or spin a smaller number of times and compare the shape of their graphs to the shape of the graph in the *Student Guide.* Is the bar for Region B about twice as tall as the bars for Regions A and C? If so, then the spinner matches the data in the graph. Students should realize that, using the appropriate spinner, the more times they spin, the more likely their data will match the graph in the *Student Guide.*

Suggestions for Teaching the Lesson

Homework and Practice

Students can use a spinner (or paper clip and pencil) at home to collect data to check a spinner. Each student can spin a given number of spins at home, record the data in a table, and add it to a class data table on the following day.

Assessment

If you have not already done so, use the *Spinners Quiz* Assessment Blackline Master to evaluate students' understanding of probability concepts.

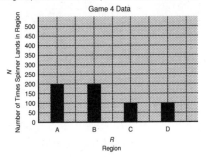

4. Design a spinner for Game 4 that you think will make data like this.

5. Choose one spinner. Test your spinner by collecting data and making a graph of the data.
   A. How many times will your group spin your spinner?
   B. Is the shape of your graph similar to the shape of the graph in the question for the spinner you have chosen? Why or why not?

Make Your Own Spinners   SG · Grade 4 · Unit 14 · Lesson 6   399

Student Guide - Page 399

AT A GLANCE

Developing the Activity

1. Students read the first page of the *Make Your Own Spinners* Activity Pages in the *Student Guide.*

2. Each student designs a spinner that he or she thinks will make data similar to Game 1 Data for *Question 1.*

3. Students design spinners to match graphs in *Questions 2–4.* Divide the class into groups. Each group can design all three spinners or focus on just one of the three spinners.

4. Students test a spinner they have designed *(Question 5).* To generate large numbers of trials, data can be pooled.

5. Students share their spinners and data with the class.

Homework

Students can continue to collect more data at home to test spinners. Have them spin a given number of spins, record the data in a table, and add it to a class data table on the following day.

Assessment

Use the *Spinners Quiz* Assessment Blackline Master to assess students' concepts of probability.

Notes:

Student Guide

Questions 1–5 (SG pp. 397–399)

1. *

2. *

3.

4. *

5. **A.** *Answers will vary.

   B. *Answers will vary. If students spin a large number of times, the shape of the graphs for their data should be similar to the shapes of the predicted graphs. The height of each bar, however, will probably not be exactly the same as the height of the corresponding bar on the predicted graph.

*Answers and/or discussion are included in the Lesson Guide.
**Answers for all the Home Practice in the *Discovery Assignment Book* are at the end of the unit.

0. Division Facts Quiz 2 (URG p. 20)

A. $10 \div 1 =$	B. $40 \div 8 =$
C. $10 \div 5 =$	D. $49 \div 7 =$
E. $70 \div 7 =$	F. $16 \div 8 =$
G. $4 \div 2 =$	H. $15 \div 5 =$
I. $20 \div 5 =$	J. $81 \div 9 =$
K. $45 \div 9 =$	L. $30 \div 3 =$
M. $12 \div 6 =$	N. $60 \div 10 =$
O. $20 \div 2 =$	P. $90 \div 9 =$

DPP Challenge is on page 77. Suggestions for using the DPPs are on page 77.

LESSON GUIDE 7

Probe Quest

Estimated
Class
Sessions:
1

This interactive book follows the adventures of two children trapped inside a video game. In order to return home, they must answer questions about probability.

Key Content

* Reviewing probability.
* Using probability to solve problems.

Materials List

Print Materials for Students

		Math Facts and Daily Practice and Problems	Activity	Homework	Written Assessment
Student Books	**Adventure Book**		*Probe Quest* Pages 71–90		
	Discovery Assignment Book			Home Practice Part 6 Page 230	
Teacher Resources	**Facts Resource Guide**	DPP Item 14O			DPP Item 14O *Division Facts Quiz 2*
	Unit Resource Guide	DPP Items O–P Pages 20–21			DPP Item O *Division Facts Quiz 2* Page 20

available on Teacher Resource CD

All Transparency Masters, Blackline Masters, and Assessment Blackline Masters in the Unit Resource Guide are on the Teacher Resource CD.

Developing the Activity

The format of this book will be familiar to many students. Periodically, they will be asked to make a choice, which will determine the next page to read. Depending on their understanding of probability, they will either move forward in the story or be required to return to the original problem.

This story can be used in several different ways. Students, individually or in pairs, may work their way through the story as a review of the probability concepts that were explored in this unit. The story may also be used by individual students as a self-assessment opportunity. Their abilities to negotiate the story will serve as indications of their understanding of probability.

Discussion Prompts

Page 76

The question on this page deals with a spinner, much like ones explored in the unit. The twins are asked the probability of a spinner landing in the green area. Since the green is one-half the area of the circle, the answer is (2), one-half.

 Probe Quest

The Quest for Level Five

SOL began to speak again, "Let us begin your journey. Each time a quest is presented, you will be given three possible answers. Choose correctly and you will find yourselves a level closer to home. Choose incorrectly and . . ."

"We may never see our home again. We understand," said Suzanne, her voice shaking. "Please begin."

"Look at the circle over there. Do you recognize it?" asked SOL.

"It looks like a probability spinner. We studied those in school," replied Joe.

"Exactly! Examine it closely, and consider your first quest. What is the probability of a spin landing in the green area?"

Choose the response you think the twins should make, then follow the instructions.

   (1) The same as spinning "red." Turn to page 82.

   (2) One-half. Turn to page 84.

   (3) One chance in three. Turn to page 83.

Adventure Book - Page 76

Probe Quest

At the end of the 10 rolls, Joe reported that a 1 had appeared three times, a 2 had appeared one time, a 3 two times, a 5 three times, and a 6 once. A 4 was never rolled.

"Very interesting information," said CUBE. "But can you use it to answer this question, 'How likely is the next roll to be a 4?'"

Choose the response you think the twins should make, then follow the instructions.

(1) It will not be a 4. Turn to page 86.

(2) The chances are one in six. Turn to page 85.

(3) It is very likely it will be a 4. Turn to page 86.

78   AB · Grade 4 · Unit 14 · Lesson 7

Discussion Prompts

Page 78

This question concerns a fair number cube. In this unit, students explored the idea that on any given roll the chance is one in six or one-sixth that a certain number will appear on the next roll. The answer is (2), the chances are one in six.

Page 81

This question may require the most thought. While they have become familiar with probability lines, the specific question posed is one they have not seen before. The problem concerns the probability that every NBA basketball player is taller than 6 feet 2 inches. While it is very likely that they are, 100% of them are not. The answer is (2), very likely.

Probe Quest

"Let us see if you can use your knowledge of this line to help you in your last quest. We are the tallest of all that exists. However, we understand there is a game often played by some tall people who reside on Level Three. It is called basketball. You are familiar with this game? We see by your nodding heads that you are. We also understand that there are men who play in something called the National Basketball Association. This is true? We see again from your nods that it is. Listen carefully. If you meet an NBA player, what is the probability that he is at least 6 feet 2 inches tall? Place this probability on the probability line."

Choose the response you think the twins should make, then follow the instructions.

(1) 100%. Turn to page 87.

(2) Very likely. Turn to page 89.

AB · Grade 4 · Unit 14 · Lesson 7   81

Suggestions for Teaching the Lesson

Homework and Practice

- Students might enjoy reading and discussing the story with an adult at home.
- Assign Part 6 of the Home Practice in the *Discovery Assignment Book*.

Answers for Part 6 of the Home Practice may be found in the Answer Key at the end of this lesson and at the end of this unit.

Assessment

DPP Bit O *Division Facts Quiz 2* is the second part of the assessment of the division facts for the twos, fives, tens, and square numbers. Bits M and O together assess all the division facts in these groups.

Extension

DPP item P provides challenging probability problems about spinners.

Language Arts Connection

Students can write their own problems to fit into the format of the story.

Name _____ Date _____

Part 6 Movie Library
Solve the following problems using appropriate tools. Explain how you solved each problem.

1. Michael, Shannon, and Jessie decided to create a movie library for their neighborhood. They asked parents and teachers to donate children's videos to create a library. Neighborhood residents could take out a children's movie for free if they brought one in as a trade. In the first week of the drive to collect movies, Michael collected 17 boxes. Each box was filled with 22 movies. How many movies did Michael collect?

2. Shannon collected 11 boxes with 27 movies in each. How many movies did Shannon collect?

3. Jessie and her friends collected 36 boxes with 15 movies in each. How many movies did they collect?

4. Approximately, how many movies did Michael, Shannon, and Jessie collect in all?

5. Jessie's little brother likes to watch the same video over and over. If the video lasts 39 minutes and he watched it 8 times in one week, about how many hours did he spend watching the video?

6. In all, 8 children worked in the movie library on Saturday. If each child helped about 30 neighborhood residents check out one movie, about how many movies were checked out on Saturday?

230 DAB · Grade 4 · Unit 14   CHANCY PREDICTIONS: AN INTRODUCTION TO PROBABILITY

Discovery Assignment Book - Page 230

Daily Practice and Problems:
Challenge for Lesson 7

P. Challenge: Probability: Spinners
(URG p. 21)

Draw a probability line on your paper. Each of the following statements has a letter in front of it. Use the letter to place the statement on the line correctly.

A. The probability of the spinner landing in Region 4.

B. The probability of the spinner landing in Region 4 or 7.

C. The probability of the spinner landing in Region 5.

D. The probability of the spinner landing in Region 2.

E. The probability of the spinner landing in Regions 1, 2, or 3.

F. The probability of the spinner landing in Region 8.

Discovery Assignment Book

**Home Practice (DAB p. 230)

Part 6. Movie Library

Questions 1–6

Strategies for *Questions 1–6* will vary.

1. 374 movies
2. 297 movies
3. 540 movies
4. One possible estimate:
   $375 + 300 + 550 = 1225$ movies
5. One possible estimate: $40 \times 8 = 320$ minutes.
   320 minutes is between 5 and $5\frac{1}{2}$ hours
6. $8 \times 30 = 240$ movies

Discovery Assignment Book

Home Practice

Part 2. School Supplies

Questions 1–4 (DAB p. 227)

1. Jessie's supplies—$7.84
   Jacob's supplies—$7.18
2. Jessie's
3. $0.66
4. Answers will vary.

Part 3. Multiplication and Division Practice

Questions A–N (DAB p. 228)

A. 4725
B. 2114
C. 9801
D. 19,644
E. 9394
F. 347
G. 4638
H. 92 R2
I. 1664 R3
J. 419 R1
K. 558
L. 1100
M. Answers will vary.
N. Answers will vary.

Part 4. Probability Lines

Questions A–J (DAB p. 229)

The placement of C, F, and H on the probability line will vary.

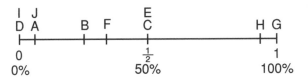

Part 5. The Power of 10

Questions A–K (DAB p. 229)

A. Answers may vary. The second factor in each problem increases by a factor of 10 each time, so there is one more zero in each of these numbers.
B. The answers will also increase by a factor of 10 each time, so there will be one more zero in each answer.
C. 4992
D. 49,920
E. 499,200
F. 4,992,000
G. 4554
H. 45,540
I. 455,400
J. 4,554,000
K. 4554; 4992; 45,540; 49,920; 455,400; 499,200; 4,554,000; 4,992,000

Part 6. Movie Library

Questions 1–6 (DAB p. 230)

Strategies for *Questions 1–6* will vary.

1. 374 movies
2. 297 movies
3. 540 movies
4. One possible estimate:
   $375 + 300 + 550 = 1225$ movies
5. One possible estimate: $40 \times 8 = 320$ minutes.
   320 minutes is between 5 and $5\frac{1}{2}$ hours
6. $8 \times 30 = 240$ movies

*Answers and/or discussion are included in the Lesson Guide.